Specific Skill Series
for Reading

Assessment Book

Sixth Edition

Columbus, OH

The McGraw-Hill Companies

Cover: (tl) © Tom Brakefield/Corbis, (tc) © Jeffrey L. Rotman/Corbis, (tr) © Randy Faris/Corbis, (cl) © Tom Brakefield/Corbis, (c, bl, br) © Photodisc/Getty Images, Inc., (cr) © Digital Vision/Getty Images, Inc., (bc) © Royalty-Free/Corbis

SRAonline.com

 SRA

Printed in the United States of America.

Send all inquiries to:
SRA/McGraw-Hill
4400 Easton Commons
Columbus, OH 43219

ISBN 0-07-603969-2

7 8 9 RHR 12 11

TABLE OF CONTENTS

Sequencing

Making Inferences

GENERAL INFORMATION AND INSTRUCTIONS

The purpose of the *Specific Skill Series for Reading Assessment Book* is to aid teachers in assessing and properly placing students within the *Specific Skill Series for Reading.*

Content

The tests consist of selections and multiple-choice questions similar to those found in the individual skill exercises within the series. The skills tested are *Using Phonics/Using Word Study, Getting the Main Idea, Finding Details, Comparing and Contrasting, Identifying Cause and Effect, Identifying Fact and Opinion, Drawing Conclusions, Sequencing,* and *Making Inferences.* There are three levels of tests: Primary, Intermediate, and Advanced.

For Whom

The Primary test is for students reading on Levels Pre-1–3. The intermediate test is for students reading on Levels 4–6. The Advanced test is for students reading on Levels 7–8.

Answer Sheets

Students should record their answers to the test on answer sheets. Blackline masters for reproducing answer sheets are included in this manual starting on page 146. There are six answer sheets in all. The first page dealing with each individual skill strand tells which answer sheet to use for each test. Refer to the Table of Contents for the page numbers. Students should be cautioned not to write in the test books.

Student Performance Profiles

A blackline master for reproducing the Student Performance Profile is included at the end of this manual. Performance Profiles let the teacher keep a cumulative record of the books that have been assigned to each student and of each student's performance in each book. When students are promoted or transferred, their profiles may be included among their records.

Administering the Test

1. Students should be instructed not to write in the test books. Teachers will provide copies of the tests and answer sheets from the blackline masters included in this manual.

2. The instructions and any tips for the skill being tested should be reviewed with the students. This information is included in the Special Instructions at the beginning of each skill strand.

3. Students should read each passage before attempting to answer the questions that follow. Except in *Finding Details,* students are allowed to reread the passage when answering the questions.

4. After students have completed the first passage and its questions, they should pause while the teacher checks to see that every student is recording each answer in the proper space on the answer sheet.

5. Students should then resume working, at their own paces. They should attempt to read all passages and complete all items. However, should they find that the material becomes too difficult, they should stop and attempt to do no more. (This applies especially to students at the lower levels of the grades for which the test is intended.)

Scoring and Placement

1. Using the appropriate answer key from this manual (pages 134–145), score each student's answer sheet.

2. Tally each student's raw score (the total number of items answered correctly). Record the raw score in the space provided on the answer sheet.

3. To determine the book level in which to place each student in the skill being tested, use the placement table for that skill.

4. Record the appropriate book level on each student's test answer sheet. In addition, record it on each student's Performance Profile.

5. When using the Intermediate or Advanced test, if a student's raw score is below the minimum score listed for that test, retest that student using the next lower level test. When using the Primary or Intermediate test, if a student's raw score is the highest possible for that level, retest that student using the next higher level test.

USING PHONICS/USING WORD STUDY

Special Instructions

1. After reading each item, students should attempt to determine the most appropriate answer choice. If any doubt exists, they should try *each* of the possible answers before making a decision.

2. It should be emphasized to students that in Items 1–12 of the Primary test students are to use *numbers* in recording their answers. Thereafter they are to use letters.

Answer Sheet Blackline Masters for tests in this skill strand:

   Primary Test: Use Answer Sheet 1.

   Intermediate Test: Use Answer Sheet 2.

   Advanced Test: Use Answer Sheet 2.

PLACEMENT TABLE

	Raw Score (Number Correct)	Book Placement
Primary Test	0–3	Picture
	4–7	Preparatory
	8–12	A
	13–19	B
	20–24	C
Intermediate Test	13–19	D
	20–33	E
	34–40	F
Advanced Test	16–33	G
	34–40	H

1. I ate a **p**___ for lunch.

2. The green **l**___ was on the tree.

3. I rode my bike on the **r**___.

4. The snail crawled on the **l**___.

5. I gave my sister a **g**___.

6. We found two **p**___ in the boat.

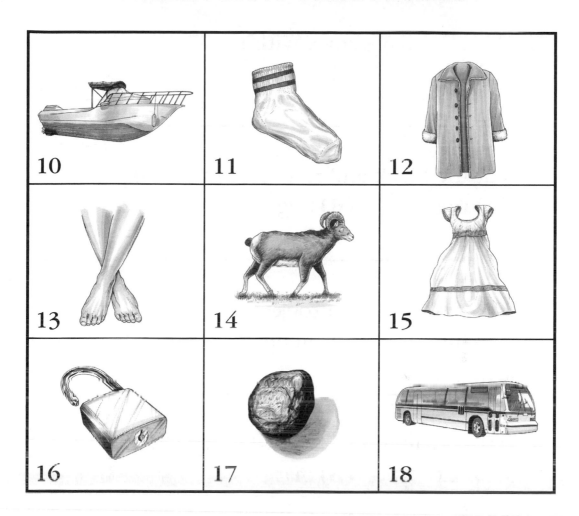

10	11	12
13	14	15
16	17	18

7. Tina rode the _____**t** on the lake.

8. I cannot find my other _____**k.**

9. A _____**m** lived in the mountains.

10. The spider lived under a _____**k.**

11. I got new shoes because my _____**t** have grown.

12. Kim wore a new _____**s** to the party.

13. Pat ___ play games with us.
(**A**) can   (**B**) ran

---

14. Put the black and red ___ in the box.
(**A**) tug   (**B**) bug

---

15. Ted will ___ on a rock.
(**A**) bump   (**B**) jump

---

16. Trish swung the ___ and hit the ball.
(**A**) bat   (**B**) mat

---

17. Mom will ___ a yellow cake.
(**A**) bake   (**B**) rake

---

18. Billy ran down the tall ___.
(**A**) pill   (**B**) hill

19. I had to **r**____ the side yard.

    (A) ead   **(B)** ake

---

20. We need to **f**____ the roof.

    (A) ix   **(B)** un

---

21. Do not **w**____ too long in line.

    (A) in   **(B)** ait

---

22. I **h**____ it rains soon.

    (A) ope   **(B)** ook

---

23. Can you **t**____ me the time?

    (A) alk   **(B)** ell

---

24. The **g**____ ate my bag.

    (A) oat   **(B)** ave

1. A new _____ was added to the street outside the school.
   (A) postcard   **(B)** crosswalk   **(C)** moonlight
   (D) backyard   **(E)** newscast   **(F)** NONE

2. The _____ display will begin at dusk.
   (A) loudspeaker **(B)** pinball   **(C)** homework
   (D) rainbow   **(E)** fireworks   **(F)** NONE

3. After all the rain, the _____ was impressive.
   (A) racketball   **(B)** suntan   **(C)** waterfall
   (D) windmill   **(E)** snowflake   **(F)** NONE

4. The _____ book will be less expensive.
   (A) everyday   **(B)** paperback   **(C)** afternoon
   (D) downtown   **(E)** sunshine   **(F)** NONE

5. One big, yellow _____ bloomed through September.
   (A) blackbird   **(B)** strawberry   **(C)** goldfish
   (D) watermelon   **(E)** sunflower   **(F)** NONE

6. The tall ships are down by the _____.
   (A) airport   **(B)** waterfront   **(C)** redwood
   (D) overpass   **(E)** ballroom   **(F)** NONE

7. My _____ keeps perfect time.
   (A) backpack   **(B)** timeout   **(C)** lifeboat
   (D) wristwatch   **(E)** afternoon   **(F)** NONE

8. The bright orange _____ clung to the coral.
   (A) spotlight   **(B)** rattlesnake   **(C)** starfish
   (D) haystack   **(E)** bulldog   **(F)** NONE

9. The _____ cleared the snow from our street.
   (A) spotlight   **(B)** touchdown   **(C)** campfire
   (D) railroad   **(E)** daydream   **(F)** NONE

10. We _____ hike down to the canyon.
   (A) whenever   **(B)** tiptoe   **(C)** somewhere
   (D) everywhere   **(E)** sometimes   **(F)** NONE

11. Open the _____, and let some light into the room.
(A) experts   (B) further   (C) whirl
(D) curtains   (E) nervous   (F) NONE

12. The garden gloves were _____.
(A) thirty   (B) turning   (C) dirty
(D) derby   (E) curly   (F) NONE

13. Mr. Collins is a tree _____.
(A) pattern   (B) turnip   (C) verse
(D) customer   (E) expert   (F) NONE

14. The boat will not turn with a broken _____.
(A) under   (B) rudder   (C) chirper
(D) burner   (E) whirler   (F) NONE

15. Please _____ left at the traffic light.
(A) nerve   (B) third   (C) advertise
(D) turn   (E) squirt   (F) NONE

16. I am _____ after eating all those pretzels.
(A) flirting   (B) purposeful   (C) thirsty
(D) further   (E) eighty   (F) NONE

17. I just missed second place and came in _____.
(A) third   (B) perfume   (C) twirl
(D) curve   (E) serve   (F) NONE

18. We watched the _____ water under the dam.
(A) modern   (B) churning   (C) furnishing
(D) thirty   (E) surrendering   (F) NONE

19. Alex had to _____ to avoid the other bicyclist.
(A) swerve   (B) purse   (C) burp
(D) stir   (E) nerve   (F) NONE

20. Do not _____ the hatching eggs.
(A) different   (B) burnish   (C) disturb
(D) corner   (E) butter   (F) NONE

21. Lashawn thought it was _____ of Tonia to eat all the candy!

   (**A**) monkish   (**B**) selfish   (**C**) prudish

   (**D**) reddish   (**E**) punish   (**F**) NONE

22. Lenny got into trouble for playing _____ while his father slept.

   (**A**) sadly   (**B**) awfully   (**C**) totally

   (**D**) rightly   (**E**) loudly   (**F**) NONE

23. It was _____ to think Latisha could save the money by Friday.

   (**A**) aimless   (**B**) heartless   (**C**) hopeless

   (**D**) sunless   (**E**) airless   (**F**) NONE

24. Albert Einstein was one of the _____ men of his time.

   (**A**) lightest   (**B**) driest   (**C**) wettest

   (**D**) biggest   (**E**) smartest   (**F**) NONE

25. Celine is the best _____ in the class because she reads a lot of books.

   (**A**) lighter   (**B**) calmer   (**C**) reader

   (**D**) sender   (**E**) folder   (**F**) NONE

26. If you _____ very hard you will learn more in school.

   (**A**) soulmate   (**B**) donate   (**C**) primate

   (**D**) obligate   (**E**) concentrate   (**F**) NONE

27. A _____ is someone who plays the harp.

   (**A**) cyclist   (**B**) scientist   (**C**) medalist

   (**D**) pianist   (**E**) harpist   (**F**) NONE

28. Lana's _____ is baking pies.

   (**A**) cruelty   (**B**) specialty   (**C**) reality

   (**D**) oddity   (**E**) eternity   (**F**) NONE

29. Carla looked out her window and saw the _____ of the night.

   (**A**) blackness   (**B**) coldness   (**C**) sunlight

   (**D**) sunless   (**E**) cordless   (**F**) NONE

30. Mother added flour to the pancake batter to _____ it.

   (**A**) brighten   (**B**) lengthen   (**C**) shorten

   (**D**) thicken   (**E**) sunken   (**F**) NONE

31. The elderly man was very _____ about his beliefs.

    (A) outspoken   **(B)** sideline   **(C)** parchment

    (D) package   **(E)** sunburst   **(F)** NONE

32. A _____ is a bad thing.

    (A) headstrong   **(B)** flotation   **(C)** cowgirl

    (D) housewife   **(E)** pitfall   **(F)** NONE

33. Carla worked on her _____ computer.

    (A) desktop   **(B)** willful   **(C)** houseboat

    (D) flamboyant   **(E)** financial   **(F)** NONE

34. Andy is studying _____ in school.

    (A) investigate   **(B)** prosecute   **(C)** geography

    (D) illustrate   **(E)** gentleness   **(F)** NONE

35. He looked at his _____ in the mirror.

    (A) memory   **(B)** childhood   **(C)** strawberry

    (D) reflection   **(E)** chocolate   **(F)** NONE

36. Your eyelid is below your _____.

    (A) signature   **(B)** eyebrow   **(C)** favorite

    (D) federal   **(E)** helicopter   **(F)** NONE

37. The baby was _____ because he missed his nap.

    (A) patchwork   **(B)** understanding **(C)** uncommon

    (D) irritable   **(E)** treatment   **(F)** NONE

38. Rain forests get _____ daily.

    (A) tablecloth   **(B)** reliable   **(C)** shortcoming

    (D) shipment   **(E)** rainfall   **(F)** NONE

39. Niagra Falls is a giant _____ between two Great Lakes.

    (A) operation   **(B)** offbeat   **(C)** symbolism

    (D) waterfall   **(E)** punishment   **(F)** NONE

40. The *Titanic* hit a large _____ that was floating in the freezing cold water.

    (A) employer   **(B)** iceberg   **(C)** agreeable

    (D) enlargement   **(E)** aardvark   **(F)** NONE

ADVANCED TEST • USING WORD STUDY

1. There is a common root in _____.
   (A) fracture   (B) incite   (C) rhapsody
       fraction   impression   rupture

2. There is a common root in _____.
   (A) emancipate   (B) candidate   (C) fragile
       marginal   camouflage   fragment

3. There is a common root in _____.
   (A) fractional   (B) indifferent   (C) pestilence
       refraction   intelligence   peculiar

4. So far all the correct answers have the roots _____.
   (A) ject/jac   (B) flect/flex   (C) fract/frag

5. The word that means "to cause to come apart or crack" is _____.
   (A) fragile   (B) fracture   (C) fragrance

6. Something that must be handled with care is _____.
   (A) fractious   (B) fragmentary   (C) fragile

7. The word that describes one part or section of a whole is _____.
   (A) franchise   (B) fraction   (C) fractus

8. A broken off piece of something is a _____.
   (A) fragment   (B) fraternal   (C) fracture

9. How many of the following words have the same root?
   fragment   infectious   fragrance   frailty   fragile   fractional
   (A) three   (B) four   (C) five

10. By using these words, you can tell that the roots **fract** and **frag** mean "_____."
    (A) mend   (B) whole   (C) small

ADVANCED TEST • USING WORD STUDY

11. Think of what **bypath, bystander,** and **byplay** mean. The prefix **by-** can mean "near, aside, or _____."
(A) in front   (B) far   (C) close

12. Think of what **byname, byway,** and **by-product** mean. The prefix **by-** can also mean "secondary, minor or _____."
(A) less important   (B) equal to   (C) more important

13. Think of what **outlive, outbid,** and **outnumber** mean. The prefix **out-** can mean "better than or _____."
(A) wealthier   (B) more than   (C) smarter

14. Think of what **outgrowth, outbound,** and **outpost** mean. The prefix **out-** can also mean "forth, away, outside, or _____."
(A) ourselves   (B) ought   (C) outward

15. Think of what **tertiary, triplicate,** and **trimester** mean. The prefixes **ter-** and **tri-** mean "occurring once every third, three, threefold, or having _____ parts."
(A) too many   (B) three   (C) matching

16. Think of what **bilingual, bifocal,** and **twice** mean. The prefixes **bi-** and **twi-** mean "_____."
(A) two   (B) cut   (C) reflection

17. Think of what **underdog, undercurrent,** and **undergrowth** mean. The prefix **under-** can mean "of a lower position, below, or _____."
(A) above   (B) beneath   (C) between

18. Think of what **underrated, undernourished,** and **underachieve** mean. The prefix **under-** can also mean "not enough or _____."
(A) below normal   (B) above normal   (C) at the right level

19. Think of what **befriend, bedraggled,** and **beguile** mean. The prefix **be-** can mean "make or _____."
(A) benefit   (B) undo   (C) cause to be

20. Think of what **benumbed, bewildered,** and **beloved** mean. The prefix **be-** can also mean "_____ or thoroughly."
(A) strong/forceful   (B) all around/all over   (C) weak/frail

21. Think of what **sanctuary, cemetery,** and **library** mean. The suffixes **-ary** and **-ery** can mean "_____."

(A) a time for   (B) a place for   (C) a record of

22. Think of what **legendary, primary,** and **military** mean. The suffix **-ary** can mean "_____."

(A) connected with   (B) outside of   (C) away from

23. Think of what **stationary, secretary,** and **missionary** mean. The suffix **-ary** can mean "_____ or that which."

(A) apart from   (B) underneath   (C) one who

24. Think of what **grammarian, vegetarian,** and **beautician** mean. The suffixes **-arian** and **-cian** mean "_____."

(A) opposite   (B) one who   (C) writing

25. Think of what **snowbound, eastbound,** and **outward-bound** mean. The suffix **-bound** means "_____."

(A) held fast or on the way to   (B) covered with   (C) breaking apart

26. Think of what **horsemanship, leadership,** and **marksmanship** mean. The suffix **-ship** can mean "_____."

(A) new at   (B) tending to   (C) art/skill

27. Think of what **readable, collectible,** and **lovable** mean. The suffixes **-able, -ible,** and **-ble** mean "_____."

(A) similar to   (B) having or being able to   (C) losing the ability to

28. Think of what **impressionable, gullible,** and **durable** mean. The suffixes **-able, -ible,** and **-ble** can also mean "_____."

(A) tending to or inclined to   (B) avoiding   (C) imitating

29. Think of what **citizenship, friendship,** and **partnership** mean. The suffix **-ship** can mean "_____ indicating the relationship specified by the related stem."

(A) phrase   (B) degree   (C) state/condition

30. Think of what **hardship, courtship,** and **worship** mean. The suffix **-ship** can also mean "process, _____, that which is formed by, or made of."

(A) action   (B) imagination   (C) knowledge

ADVANCED TEST • USING WORD STUDY

31. Think of what **unify, unit,** and **unicycle** mean. The prefix **uni-** means "_____."

   (A) separate   **(B)** one   **(C)** under

32. Think of what **clockwise, counterclockwise,** and **lengthwise** mean. The suffix **-wise** means "manner or _____."

   (A) time   **(B)** operation   **(C)** direction

33. Think of what **motion, mobility,** and **movable** mean. The roots **mot, mob,** and **mov** mean "_____."

   (A) move   **(B)** still   **(C)** shape

34. Think of what **aquarium, terrarium,** and **planetarium** mean. The suffix **-ium** means "_____."

   (A) important   **(B)** place   **(C)** state of

35. Think of what **aquatic, aquifer,** and **aqueous** mean. The root **aqua** means "_____."

   (A) air   **(B)** soil   **(C)** water

36. Think of what **midsummer, midstream,** and **midway** mean. The prefix **mid-** means "_____."

   (A) under   **(B)** middle   **(C)** over

37. Think of what **autograph, geography,** and **photograph** mean. The roots **graph** and **graphy** mean "something written or a _____."

   (A) record   **(B)** technology   **(C)** change

38. Think of what **outnumber, outshine,** and **outperform** mean. The prefix **out-** means "more than or _____ than."

   (A) better   **(B)** nicer   **(C)** wiser

39. Think of what **gradual, graduate,** and **progressive** mean. The roots **grad** and **gress** mean "_____."

   (A) break   **(B)** slowness   **(C)** step

40. Think of what **vegetarian, veterinarian,** and **pediatrician** mean. The suffixes **-arian** and **-cian** mean "_____ who."

   (A) none   **(B)** one   **(C)** animals

GETTING THE MAIN IDEA

Special Instructions

After reading each passage, students should select its main idea from the answer choices. The choices are below the selections in Exercises 1–4 in the Primary test and on the opposite page thereafter.

Answer Sheet Blackline Masters for tests in this skill strand:

Primary Test: Use Answer Sheet 3.

Intermediate Test: Use Answer Sheet 4.

Advanced Test: Use Answer Sheet 4.

PLACEMENT TABLE

	Raw Score (Number Correct)	Book Placement
Primary Test	0–1	Picture
	2	Preparatory
	3–4	A
	5–6	B
	7–8	C
Intermediate Test	3–4	D
	5–7	E
	8–10	F
Advanced Test	5–7	G
	8–10	H

Bianca could not decide what to wear to the costume party. "Why don't you go as a clown?" her mother asked.

Bianca thought it was a good idea. She found an old smock and gardening hat. She went to the store and bought makeup. She drew large white eyebrows and a red nose and mouth. Her costume was so good no one knew who she was when she arrived at the party!

1. What is the main idea?
  (A) Bianca dressed up as a clown for the costume party.
  (B) Bianca wore an old smock and gardening hat.
  (C) Bianca drew a large red nose and mouth on her face.

Joseph loves to work in his garden. He works on it every day. He bought a tree today. He will have to dig a big hole for the roots. He will plant it on the weekend. Joseph will only water his flowers today. He will leave the tree on his porch to plant on Saturday.

2. What is the main idea?
  (A) Joseph bought a tree today.
  (B) Joseph works on his garden every day.
  (C) Joseph will leave the tree on his porch.

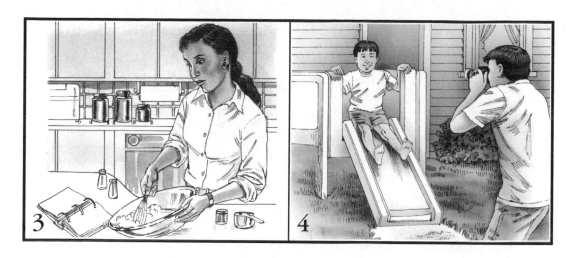

Luisa wanted to make breakfast for her family. She found the foods she needed. When the family got up the next morning, the house smelled good. Food was on the table. "Where did this come from?" asked Mother. Luisa smiled. Everyone enjoyed the food.

3. What is the main idea?

(A) There was food on the table.

(B) Luisa made breakfast for the family.

(C) The house smelled good.

"Stay still," said Soto. "I am going to take a picture." When Soto took the picture, Jon made a funny face.

Soto did not like the picture. He told Jon not to make a funny face. Then Soto took another picture. This time Soto liked the picture.

4. What is the main idea?

(A) Soto took Jon's picture.

(B) Jon made a funny face.

(C) Soto did not like the first picture.

5.   Ms. Ross took the letters from the mailbox and went into her house. She put the letters behind the television. Ms. Ross has to hide her mail because her dog eats it.

---

6.   You hike up and down hills. It works your legs. You breathe harder. You get stronger. You feel better after your hike.

---

7.   The deer were in the grass. They saw the campers. The deer went into the woods. A sound made them run far. They wanted to get away from the campers.

---

8.   "He is eating a grape," said Kyle. Then the monkey picked up an apple. "Look at it eat that apple. Now it wants that corn!" said Kyle. He watched the monkey eat and eat.

5. What it is the main idea?

(A) The dog is hungry.

(B) The dog likes to play hide-and-seek.

(C) Ms. Ross hides the mail from her dog.

---

6. What is the main idea?

(A) Hiking is good exercise.

(B) People need strong legs.

(C) It is good to breathe hard.

---

7. What is the main idea?

(A) Deer stay in the woods.

(B) Deer stay away from people.

(C) Campers see deer all the time.

---

8. What is the main idea?

(A) A monkey will eat many things.

(B) Kyle likes to eat.

(C) The monkey can hold a grape.

1.   Ancient Egyptians had a hieroglyphic writing system. Hieroglyphs are pictures used to express ideas. These picture words were carved on walls where people gathered. They told stories about the Egyptian rulers and animals. The picture words were also used to keep records of taxes and other business information.

---

2.   Ice cream comes in many different and interesting flavors. Sometimes ice cream is made with a crust on the outside. In Italy and France ice cream usually contains nuts and fruit. There are many recipes for garlic-flavored ice cream. Other unique flavors include avocado, sweet corn, and jalapeño.

---

3.   People with blond hair at a college in Massachusetts had a surprise one day. Their hair turned green! The town had put a new chemical into the water. The town stopped using the chemical. Those with green hair washed their hair with special shampoo and became blond again.

---

4.   One day Officer Murphy said that he could ride his bicycle as fast as a railroad train. In those days trains could travel sixty miles per hour. A race against a train was planned. Murphy won the race. He had raced faster than sixty miles per hour. The newspapers made him famous as "Mile-a-Minute Murphy."

---

5.   More than one hundred years ago, the state of Nebraska had few trees. Julius Morton, a newspaper writer, asked everyone to plant trees on April 10, 1872. He called that day Arbor Day. People planted more than one million trees. Soon other states around Nebraska began to have Arbor Days too.

1. The story is mainly about
   (A) many different forms of writing.
   (B) the history of Egypt.
   (C) the uses of hieroglyphics.

2. The story is mainly about
   (A) how ice cream is made.
   (B) unusual flavors of ice cream.
   (C) Italian ice cream.

3. The story is mainly about
   (A) why blond people use shampoo.
   (B) what happened when a new chemical was put into the water.
   (C) a small college in Massachusetts.

4. The story is mainly about
   (A) the history of railroad trains.
   (B) the history of bicycles.
   (C) Officer Murphy's amazing racing feat.

5. The story is mainly about
   (A) Nebraska in the 1800s.
   (B) why people like trees.
   (C) how Arbor Day began.

6.   In 1853 Levi Strauss went to California with one roll of heavy brown canvas. The gold miners wanted sturdy pants that could hold up to hard work. Strauss used the canvas to make pants. Everyone wanted "those Levi's pants." Strauss was in business. Today denim replaces canvas, but the style is still the same.

7.   The *Mayflower* was the ship that carried the Pilgrims from England to America. It was used for the next few years until it became too timeworn to sail. It returned to England. Someone took the ship apart and used the wood to make a barn. The barn still stands in Buckingham.

8.   An angler is someone who fishes with a hook and line. The anglerfish has a "fishing rod" that grows from its head and hangs in front of its mouth. The "rod" is shiny and attracts other fish. When a fish swims close, the anglerfish snaps up another meal!

9.   Long ago, people had to pay taxes on some strange things. In New York anyone who wore a wig had to pay a tax. Russia had a tax on beards. In Holland people had to pay a tax for every window in their house, so people began building houses without windows.

10.   Some people have strange watch "dogs." One family in Michigan has a watch rabbit. A store in Indiana is guarded by a lion cub. One Swedish business scares off burglars with a giant boa constrictor snake. Geese, crows, falcons, and alligators also protect stores and homes.

6. The story is mainly about
(A) gold miners' clothing.
(B) the history of California.
(C) Levi's pants.

---

7. The story is mainly about
(A) the barns in England.
(B) the Pilgrims coming to America.
(C) the history of the *Mayflower*.

---

8. The story is mainly about
(A) a fish that fishes for fish.
(B) choosing bait.
(C) freshwater fishing.

---

9. The story is mainly about
(A) growing beards.
(B) strange taxes of long ago.
(C) building houses without windows.

---

10. The story is mainly about
(A) how rabbits imitate dogs.
(B) animals used as guards.
(C) boa constrictors.

1. A hurricane is a large and powerful storm that starts over warm ocean water. It causes strong and damaging winds. Hurricanes form in all parts of the world. They are known by many different names. Scientists often use the term "tropical storm." In the Indian Ocean they are referred to as cyclones. Each year a handful of thunderstorms over the Atlantic Ocean develop into hurricanes. The greatest number of tropical storms occur in the northern Pacific, where they are known as typhoons. **Typhoon** is the Chinese word for "great wind." Hurricanes near Australia are called willy-willies.

2. Many of the things we use on a daily basis originated in another country. Hundreds of them came from Italy. Do you have windows in your house? Long ago, glass windowpanes were invented in Italy. The Italians invented concrete and made the first paved roads. Newspapers were their idea, as well as clocks and radios. The first public schools started in Italy 1,900 years ago. Many people know that pizza and mozzarella cheese came from Italy, but so did pretzels and cookies. Italians invented thermometers, batteries, and forks. People in Italy wore the first socks, but 1,600 years ago they were made of leather!

3. Palominos are horses that are grouped according to their color, not their breed. Many kinds of horses can be palominos if their coloring is right. To be a palomino, a horse has to be the same color as a new gold dollar coin. The skin under its hair must be dark or golden. A palomino's mane and tail must be almost completely white. A palomino can have only certain markings on its face and lower legs. A horse that has a black mane, spotted skin, blue eyes, or streaks on its hair cannot be a palomino.

4. The Great Pyramid in Egypt is 485 feet tall and made of three million stone blocks, each weighing three tons. Historians are baffled as to how the ancient Egyptians built this massive structure. They think it may have taken thousands of workers twenty years to build. There are two hundred layers of stone, and the ancient Egyptians didn't have lifting machines. Some say they made temporary spiral ramps of mud and pulled the stones on sleds. Others think they used one huge ramp. Some suggest that they lifted every stone up the sides with a lever. Perhaps they had more technology than we realize.

5. In the late 1800s major-league baseball players had to be white. One manager thought that was unfair. He searched for a talented African American ballplayer to break the "color barrier." He found Jackie Robinson. Robinson played his first game with the Brooklyn Dodgers in 1947. He impressed people with his daring style. His teammates respected him, but many "fans" were hateful. He faced nasty insults and threats to his family. Pitchers even threw at his head. He never gave up. In 1949 he became the league MVP. Robinson opened doors for thousands of minority athletes.

ADVANCED TEST • GETTING THE MAIN IDEA

1. The story is mainly about
   (A) how a hurricane is formed.
   (B) why hurricanes occur all over the world.
   (C) which word for **hurricane** is the best choice.
   (D) what hurricanes are called around the world.

2. The story is mainly about
   (A) Italy long ago.
   (B) why we use so many inventions from Italy.
   (C) the many countries from which things originated.
   (D) everyday things that were invented in Italy.

3. The story is mainly about
   (A) palominos being grouped according to their breed.
   (B) palominos being the world's most valuable horse.
   (C) what a horse must look like to be a palomino.
   (D) what markings a palomino can have on its face and legs.

4. The story is mainly about
   (A) how the ancient Egyptians built the Great Pyramid.
   (B) how the ancient Egyptians might have built the Great Pyramid.
   (C) why the ancient Egyptians built the Great Pyramid.
   (D) why the theory of the spiral ramps makes the most sense.

5. The story is mainly about
   (A) how Jackie Robinson broke baseball's color barrier.
   (B) how horrible people were to Jackie Robinson.
   (C) why major-league baseball had a rule that only white people could play.
   (D) how Jackie Robinson responded when people were hateful to him.

6.   *Robinson Crusoe* is a story about a man stranded on an island for many years. He had to make his own shelter and get his own food. Many readers don't know that *Robinson Crusoe* is based on a true adventure. A man named Alexander Selkirk once spent five lonely years on an island. The island was 360 miles off the coast of South America. Selkirk caught lobsters and ate fruits and vegetables. He built his own shelter and made his own clothes of goatskin. After his rescue, many stories were written about him. The most famous was *Robinson Crusoe.*

7.   Clara Barton, born in 1821, worked first as a teacher and then served as a nurse at Civil War battle lines. She served similarly in the Franco-Prussian War in Europe. It was in Europe that Barton heard about the recently organized International Red Cross. On returning to the United States, Barton organized the American National Red Cross, serving as its president until 1904. She was responsible for the provision that permitted the Red Cross to provide relief in times of natural disasters, such as floods, as well as in wartime. The results of Clara Barton's extraordinary efforts are still being felt.

8.   The soybean is one of the most important crops in North America. In addition to the soybean's numerous uses as a food, soybean by-products are used to make cosmetics, paints, plastics, and fire-extinguisher foam. The late Henry Ford was a great fan of the soybean. He liked to wear clothes made of soybean fibers, and he used soybeans to manufacture many car parts. However, he stopped short of manufacturing an entire automobile out of soybeans— perhaps because a goat once ate a license plate made of soybean fiberboard.

9.   There were many African American cowhands in the West during the last century. As many as five thousand of them worked as cattle drivers along the trails. But Mulzim Fida'i is different—he's a rodeo cowhand. He enjoyed Western movies as a child and loved to rig himself out in full cowhand gear. When he got out of the Marine Corps in the late 1960s, he worked in construction and rode horses for fun. He went around to rodeos and was finally encouraged to enter the steer-wrestling contests. He was successful until he injured both knees. Today he is planning to start a rodeo school near New York City so other city children can learn to become rodeo cowhands.

10.   Pilots Dick Rutan and Jeana Yeager left Edwards Air Force Base on December 14, 1986, in the experimental light plane *Voyager.* On December 23, they returned with only a few gallons of fuel left. Along the way, they got little rest. They constantly had to monitor their autopilot and radios, check the oil system, check the fuel supply, and navigate. They had expected to be able to put the plane on autopilot for extended periods and get some sleep. Instead, after an hour an alarm would go off, telling them that the plane was climbing. Yeager and Rutan set an aviation record that can never be broken: the first nonstop flight around the world without refueling!

6. This story is mainly about

   (A) why Alexander Selkirk made his clothes from goatskin.

   (B) how to survive on a deserted island.

   (C) how *Robinson Crusoe* was based on the life of Alexander Selkirk.

   (D) an island 360 miles off the coast of South America.

---

7. This story is mainly about

   (A) how Clara Barton's humanitarian efforts are still being felt.

   (B) why the Red Cross is a successful organization.

   (C) how to get involved with the Red Cross.

   (D) Clara Barton's nursing career.

---

8. This story is mainly about

   (A) why Henry Ford never made an entire car out of soybeans.

   (B) Henry Ford's soybean license plate.

   (C) how to make fire-extinguisher foam from a soybean.

   (D) the soybean and its many uses and by-products.

---

9. This story is mainly about

   (A) steer-wrestling contests.

   (B) cowhands in the West during the twentieth century.

   (C) Mulzim Fida'i, an African American cowhand.

   (D) a school for cowhands located in New York City.

---

10. This story is mainly about

   (A) the *Voyager*.

   (B) the first nonstop flight around the world without refueling.

   (C) Edwards Air Force Base.

   (D) how to fly a plane on autopilot.

FINDING DETAILS

Special Instructions

1. Students should first read the entire passage slowly and carefully.

2. After completing the passage, students should turn to the questions and choose the correct answer to each. It must be emphasized to students that they may not refer back to the passage and that there is only one correct answer to each question: the one found in the passage. Other answers to a question may be true from the student's own knowledge or experience, but no answer is considered correct unless it is in the passage.

Answer Sheet Blackline Masters for tests in this skill strand:

    Primary Test: Use Answer Sheet 4.

    Intermediate Test: Use Answer Sheet 5.

    Advanced Test: Use Answer Sheet 5.

PLACEMENT TABLE

	Raw Score (Number Correct)	Book Placement
Primary Test	0–2	Picture
	3–4	Preparatory
	5–6	A
	7–8	B
	9–10	C
Intermediate Test	4–10	D
	11–15	E
	16–20	F
Advanced Test	8–13	G
	14–20	H

Tino's mom asked him to go to the store. She told him what to buy. Tino rode his bicycle to the store.

Tino bought some apples at the store. He bought some dog food too. Then he went back home.

Tino fed the dog. Then his mom asked, "Tino, where is the newspaper? I want to read it." Tino knew he forgot to buy something! He went back to the store to get it.

PRIMARY TEST • FINDING DETAILS

1. Where did Tino go in the story?
   (A) Grandma's house
   (B) A barbershop
   (C) The store

---

2. Who asked Tino to go to the store?
   (A) His grandma
   (B) His mom
   (C) His dad

---

3. How did Tino get to the store?
   (A) He rode his bicycle.
   (B) He took a bus.
   (C) He drove the car.

---

4. What two things did Tino buy at the store?
   (A) Apples and dog food
   (B) Apples and bananas
   (C) Grapes and dog food

---

5. What did Tino forget to buy at the store?
   (A) Apples
   (B) Dog food
   (C) A newspaper

Juan likes to fish. One day it was so cold that ice was on the water. Juan cut a hole in the ice and began to fish. Soon Juan caught a big fish. He tried to get the fish out of the water. He could not. The hole in the ice was too little. The next time Juan went fishing, he cut a bigger hole in the ice.

6. What does Juan like to do?
(A) Play guitar
(B) Read
(C) Fish

---

7. In the story, what was on the water?
(A) Leaves
(B) Ice
(C) Lily pads

---

8. What did Juan catch?
(A) A big fish
(B) A cold
(C) A little fish

---

9. Why couldn't Juan get the fish out of the water?
(A) The hole in the ice was too big.
(B) The hole in the ice was too small.
(C) He did not cut a hole in the ice.

---

10. What was Juan going to do the next time he went fishing?
(A) Cut a smaller hole in the ice
(B) Cut a bigger hole in the ice
(C) Use different bait

In southern Ohio, clusters of dirt mounds stand in the middle of farm fields. Who created these earthworks? Why were they built? How long have they stood?

From A.D. 200 to 500, the Ohio River Valley was the home of prehistoric Native Americans known as the Hopewell. The most obvious traces of the Hopewell culture lie along the Scioto River near Chillicothe, Ohio. In this area, earth walls surround a group of 23 mounds in the form of squares, circles, and other geometric shapes. Historians refer to this group of mounds as the Mound City Group.

Careful digging around the mounds in the 1840s revealed important information about the Hopewell. The mounds appear to be places of burial, not places where people once lived. Objects found inside the mounds show that the Hopewell were an advanced people who traded far and wide. Seashells from the Gulf of Mexico, shark teeth from the Chesapeake Bay, copper and silver from the Great Lakes region, and mica from the Blue Ridge Mountains of North Carolina were found. Two hundred stone pipes were found in one mound. The bowls of the pipes had been skillfully carved into figures of animals, birds, and reptiles. In other mounds were clay pottery, copper tools, stone spearheads, silver headpieces, and strings of shells and freshwater pearls.

The Hopewell people lived outside the mounds in small settlements along the Scioto River. The river provided food, water, and transportation. If their food source became scarce, a settlement would move to a different area where the food was plentiful.

During World War I, Mound City was used as part of an army training camp. Consequently, many of the mounds were destroyed. Soon after the war, the mounds were restored using the careful measurements taken in the 1840s. In 1992, the Mound City Group, along with several other earthworks in the area, became Hopewell Culture National Historical Park.

The Hopewell culture ended about 1,500 years ago. Within a few hundred years, other cultures moved into the fertile river valleys. Today the great mounds stand to remind us of the once-thriving Hopewell culture.

INTERMEDIATE TEST • FINDING DETAILS

1. Where are the most obvious traces of the Hopewell culture?
  (A) Near the Gulf of Mexico
  (B) Along the Scioto River near Chillicothe, Ohio
  (C) In the Great Lakes region

2. When did the Hopewell live in the Ohio Valley?
  (A) A.D. 200–500   **(B)** 1200–1550   **(C)** 1939–1945

3. How many Hopewell mounds are there in all?
  (A) 12   **(B)** 23   **(C)** 32

4. How do historians refer to the group of mounds?
  (A) The Scioto Mound
  (B) Village of the Mounds
  (C) Mound City Group

5. How were the mounds once used?
  (A) As burial sites
  (B) As storage places
  (C) As homes for several families

6. What do we know about the Hopewell?
  (A) They lived in Ohio in the 1800s.
  (B) They lived beneath the mounds.
  (C) They traded far and wide.

7. When did historians first start digging around the mounds?
  (A) 1490s   **(B)** 1840s   **(C)** 1960s

8. What did the Hopewell do if game became scarce?
  (A) Moved to a different area where there was more food
  (B) Changed their diets
  (C) Asked other tribes for food

9. How were the mounds destroyed at one point?
  (A) The Scioto River flooded and washed them away.
  (B) An army training camp was set up on the grounds.
  (C) People dug into the mounds looking for treasure.

10. What happened to the Mound City Group in 1992?
  (A) It became part of the Hopewell Culture National Historical Park.
  (B) It was completely rebuilt according to earlier measurements.
  (C) It was closed to the public for ten years.

If you visit Niagara Falls, you can take a ride on a tour boat named the *Maid of the Mist*. Actually, there are several boats with that name. One of them sails every fifteen minutes during the day. The boat trip is so popular that you probably will have to wait in line. But the ride is worth the wait. After you board the boat, head for the railing. That way you will have an excellent view.

Be sure to put on the blue plastic raincoat that you are given. It will help keep you dry. Still, even with the raincoat, you can get very wet! After you have donned your raincoat, look around. You will see that the other visitors are also wearing their raincoats.

The ship has now begun to move away from the dock. The engines are loud and are working hard. The boat is going against a very strong current as it heads toward the first waterfall.

Niagara Falls consists of three different waterfalls. The first waterfall you will pass is the American Falls. The next is the narrow Bridal Veil Falls. Finally you will head toward the largest of the three. It is called the Horseshoe Falls.

The closer you get to the falls, the rockier the ride becomes. As the *Maid of the Mist* nears the Horseshoe Falls, the spray from the water seems to come at you from every direction. The sound of the falls roars in your ears. The roar is so loud that you can no longer hear the boat's engines.

As the boat heads back toward the dock, it seems steadier. The water is calmer. You can hear people's voices again. It is hard to believe that only a half hour has passed.

11. The name of the tour boat is the *Maid of the*

    (A) *Falls.*   **(B)** *Mist.*   **(C)** *Niagara.*

12. A tour boat sails every

    (A) 15 minutes.   **(B)** 20 minutes.   **(C)** 30 minutes.

13. You will have an excellent view from the

    (A) engines.   **(B)** dock.   **(C)** railing.

14. Everyone is given a

    (A) blue raincoat.

    (B) white raincoat.

    (C) yellow raincoat.

15. When the boat is heading toward the falls, it is going

    (A) with the current.

    (B) against the current.

    (C) toward the dock.

16. Niagara Falls consists of

    (A) one waterfall.

    (B) two waterfalls.

    (C) three waterfalls.

17. The largest waterfall is

    (A) the American Falls.

    (B) Bridal Veil Falls.

    (C) the Horseshoe Falls.

18. The first waterfall you will pass is

    (A) the American Falls.

    (B) Bridal Veil Falls.

    (C) the Horseshoe Falls.

19. As you near the falls, the ride becomes

    (A) calmer.   **(B)** rockier.   **(C)** smoother.

20. The boat trip takes

    (A) a half hour.

    (B) an hour.

    (C) fifteen minutes.

ADVANCED TEST • FINDING DETAILS

The village of Vestmannaeyjar, in the far northern country of Iceland, is as bright, clean, and up-to-date as any American or Canadian suburb. It is located on the island of Heimaey, just off the mainland. One January night in 1973, however, households were shocked from their sleep. In some backyards, red-hot liquid was spurting from the ground. Flaming "skyrockets" shot up and over the houses. The island's volcano, Helgafell, silent for seven thousand years, was erupting violently!

Luckily, the island's fishing fleet was in port, and within twenty-four hours almost everyone was ferried to the mainland. Then the condition on the island began to worsen. Fountains of burning lava spurted three hundred feet high. Black, baseball-sized cinders rained down. A cloud of dark smoke and gas erupted into the air, and a river of lava flowed down the mountain. The constant high-pitched whistle of escaping steam was punctuated by booming explosions.

As time passed, the once-pleasant village of Vestmannaeyjar took on a weird aspect. Its street lamps still burning against the long arctic night, the town lay under a thick blanket of cinders. All that could be seen above the ten-foot black drifts were the tips of street signs. Some houses had collapsed under the weight of cinders; others had burst into flames as the heat ignited their oil-storage tanks. Lighting the whole lurid scene, fire continued to shoot from the mouth of the looming volcano.

The eruption continued for six months. Scientists and reporters arrived from around the world to observe the awesome natural event.

But the townspeople did not give up easily. In July, when the eruption ceased, the people of Heimaey Island returned to assess the chances of rebuilding their homes and lives. They found tons of ash covering the ground. The Icelanders are tough people, however, accustomed to the strange and violent nature of their arctic land. They dug out their homes. They even used the cinders to build new roads and airport runways. Now the new homes of Heimaey are warmed from water pipes heated by molten lava.

ADVANCED TEST • FINDING DETAILS

1. This village is located on the island of
   (A) Vestmannaeyjar.
   (B) Hebrides.
   (C) Heimaey.
   (D) Helgafell.

2. The name of the volcano is
   (A) Vestmannaeyjar.
   (B) Hebrides.
   (C) Heimaey.
   (D) Helgafell.

3. The liquid was coming from the
   (A) mountains.
   (B) ground.
   (C) sea.
   (D) sky.

4. The island's volcano had been inactive for
   (A) seventy years.
   (B) seven thousand years.
   (C) seven thousand months.
   (D) seven hundred years.

5. The islanders were evacuated within twenty-four
   (A) hours.
   (B) days.
   (C) minutes.
   (D) weeks.

6. Black cinders fell that were the size of
   (A) baseballs.
   (B) pebbles.
   (C) golf balls.
   (D) footballs.

7. Despite the eruption
   (A) buses kept running.
   (B) the radio kept broadcasting.
   (C) the police kept working.
   (D) street lamps kept burning.

8. This volcanic eruption lasted for
   (A) weeks.
   (B) hours.
   (C) months.
   (D) days.

9. The eruption finally ended in the month of
   (A) June.
   (B) January.
   (C) August.
   (D) July.

10. To rebuild roads the people used
    (A) lava.
    (B) bricks.
    (C) cement.
    (D) cinders.

Have you heard about a kind of grass that grows as tall as the tallest trees? What about a grass that can be made as strong as steel? Houses, furniture, boats, and hundreds of other useful things can be made from this type of grass. You would even enjoy eating this type of grass! That grass is bamboo, the "wood" of 1,001 uses.

Bamboo may look like wood, but it is part of the wheat, oats, and barley family. It is a kind of grass. This grass is not just a material for making useful products. Young bamboo is eaten, often mixed with other vegetables, in many Asian foods.

Bamboo grows in many parts of the world. In the United States it grows in an area from Virginia, west to Indiana, and south to Florida, Louisiana, and Texas. Most bamboo, however, is found in warm, wet climates, especially in Asia and on the islands of the South Pacific Ocean.

In most Asian countries, bamboo is nearly as important as rice. Many Asians live in bamboo houses. They sit on bamboo chairs and sleep on bamboo mats. They fence their land with bamboo and use its wood for cages for chickens and pigs.

Bamboo is used to build large buildings as well as homes. When it is glued in layers, it becomes as strong as steel. On some islands in the South Pacific, bamboo is even used for water pipes.

This extraordinary material has many other uses. It is used to make musical instruments, such as flutes and recorders. Paper made from bamboo has been highly prized by artists for thousands of years.

Bamboo is light and strong, and it bends without breaking. It is cheap, floats on water, almost never wears out, and is easy to grow.

Nothing else on Earth grows quite as fast as bamboo. At times you can even see it grow! Botanists, people who study plants, have recorded growth of more than three feet in just twenty-four hours! Bamboo is hollow and has a strong root system that almost never stops growing and spreading. In fact, only after it flowers, an event that may happen only once every thirty years, will bamboo die.

There are more than a thousand kinds of bamboo. The smallest is only three inches tall and one-tenth of an inch wide. The largest reaches more than two hundred feet in height and seven inches in diameter.

It is no wonder, then, that the lives of nearly half the people on Earth would change enormously if there were no longer any bamboo. It is no wonder, too, that to many people bamboo is a symbol of happiness and good fortune.

ADVANCED TEST • FINDING DETAILS

11. One of the world's most useful "woods" is
    (A) bamboo.   **(B)** oak.
    (C) pine.   **(D)** balsa.

12. Most bamboo grows in
    (A) the United States.   **(B)** Canada.
    (C) South America.   **(D)** Asia and the islands of the South Pacific.

13. Bamboo grows best in
    (A) cool, dry climates.   **(B)** mountain regions.
    (C) warm, wet climates.   **(D)** desert regions.

14. In the United States, bamboo grows in
    (A) Maine.   **(B)** Texas.
    (C) Illinois.   **(D)** Oregon.

15. To Asians, bamboo is
    (A) too costly to grow.   **(B)** mainly used as a food.
    (C) the most important crop.   **(D)** nearly as important as rice.

16. As a plant bamboo is
    (A) hard to grow.   **(B)** slow-growing.
    (C) fast-growing.   **(D)** found only in Asia.

17. Bamboo is really
    (A) a kind of tree.   **(B)** used in place of rice as a food.
    (C) a low-growing bush.   **(D)** a type of grass.

18. Bamboo may flower about once every
    (A) five years.   **(B)** thirty years.
    (C) twenty years.   **(D)** ten years.

19. The tallest kinds of bamboo reach a height of
    (A) three inches.   **(B)** seven inches.
    (C) two hundred feet.   **(D)** one hundred feet.

20. Bamboo is important to
    (A) all the people on Earth.   **(B)** half the people of Asia.
    (C) half the people on Earth.   **(D)** only a few people.

COMPARING & CONTRASTING

Special Instructions

1. Students should read the passages slowly and carefully. Encourage students to visualize the descriptions of the people or things in each passage to more fully understand how they are alike or different.

2. After reading the passage, students should recall details of how things compare or contrast to find the best answer to each question.

Answer Sheet Blackline Masters for tests in this skill strand:

   Primary Test: Use Answer Sheet 3.

   Intermediate Test: Use Answer Sheet 4.

   Advanced Test: Use Answer Sheet 4.

PLACEMENT TABLE

	Raw Score (Number Correct)	Book Placement
Primary Test	0–1	Picture
	2	Preparatory
	3–4	A
	5–6	B
	7–8	C
Intermediate Test	3–4	D
	5–7	E
	8–10	F
Advanced Test	5–7	G
	8–10	H

Sara and Ida went to the ice rink. Sara skated on one foot. Then she skated fast and did a spin. Ida skated slowly around the rink. She held onto the railing so she wouldn't fall. Finally, the two friends went home. "That was fun!" Sara said to Ida.

1. From the story you can tell that

    (A) Ida is a better skater than Sara.

    (B) Sara is a better skater than Ida.

    (C) ice-skating is fun.

Every morning we eat toast. I put butter on my toast. My sister puts jelly on her toast. My brother eats his toast plain.

2. From the story you can tell that

    (A) all the children eat jelly.

    (B) all the children eat toast.

    (C) all the children eat butter.

Jim and Jed are twins. Their friends cannot tell them apart. Both boys have big green eyes and short red hair. Each day they dress in the same shirts and pants. But the boys are not the same at all. Jim likes to play sports and beat on his drum set. Jed likes to read books and draw trains and jets. The boys may be twins, but each is one of a kind.

3. How are the boys the same?

   (A) Both play sports and read books.

   (B) Both play drums and draw things.

   (C) Both have green eyes and short red hair.

Manuel had soup for lunch. His friend Seamus had a slice of pizza.

"Do you want to trade our lunches?" asked Manuel.

"Okay," said Seamus. "Let's trade our snacks too!"

4. From the story you can tell that

   (A) Manuel likes Seamus's lunch better.

   (B) Manuel likes his own lunch better.

   (C) Manuel does not like eating lunch.

5.   Monday the sun was shining brightly, and there was a warm breeze. The sky was blue with just a few fluffy white clouds. Tuesday it was rainy and cool. The wind was blowing, and the sky was dark gray.

___

6.   Ed likes to play chess. He plays chess every day with his friend. Ted likes to play baseball. He plays baseball every day with his friends. Both boys are in the second grade and go to the same school.

___

7.   Mia has long straight hair. She spends a lot of time brushing it. In the morning it takes ten minutes to braid her hair. Carla has short curly hair. She brushes it quickly in the morning before she goes to school. Both girls have brown hair.

___

8.   My dog Ollie is so small I can pick him up and carry him when we go for walks. Ollie sits on my lap while I pet him. My friend has a big dog named Buster. Buster is so big he drags my friend down the street when she takes him for walks. I like small dogs, and my friend likes big dogs. However, both of us love our dogs.

5. What is the difference between Monday and
Tuesday?

(**A**) Monday was warm, while Tuesday was cool.

(**B**) Monday was windy, while Tuesday was not.

(**C**) Monday was rainy, while Tuesday was not.

---

6. How are the boys different?

(**A**) Both are in second grade.

(**B**) Ed likes to play chess, and Ted likes to play
baseball.

(**C**) Ed plays every day, and Ted does not.

---

7. How are Mia and Carla different?

(**A**) Carla has brown hair, and Mia does not.

(**B**) Mia has long hair, and Carla has short hair.

(**C**) Mia brushes her hair in the morning, and Carla
does not.

---

8. How are the dogs different?

(**A**) One dog goes for walks, but the other does not.

(**B**) Ollie is big, and Buster is small.

(**C**) One dog is big, and the other is small.

INTERMEDIATE TEST • COMPARING & CONTRASTING

1.   Many people use simple push mowers to cut the grass. Push mowers require a person to push them across the lawn. A round blade turns and cuts the grass. Push mowers do not have motors, so they don't need gasoline like regular lawn mowers do. That makes them much quieter too!

2.   Friends say Adam and Joseph are as different as night and day. Adam has brown hair and is quiet. Joseph has blond hair and is very talkative. These two brothers actually have more in common than people realize. Both like to build things out of wood, ride their bikes together, and go fishing with their dad.

3.   Downhill skiing and cross-country skiing are two winter sports that require skis, poles, special boots, and snow. In downhill skiing, skiers zip quickly down steep slopes. Cross-country skiers travel on flatter trails through woods or fields. The quick, fast strides that cross-country skiers make provide great exercise and body warmth.

4.   Parks are wonderful places to visit. A national forest park is big and allows dogs. It does not have much in the way of facilities, but it has miles of trails through salt marshes and woodlands. By contrast, a state park with its camp store, showers, and washing stations is great for family camping.

5.   Field hockey, played on a large field, has eleven players. Ice hockey has only six players on the ice at one time. Both sports use sticks to hit a ball or puck into the opposing goal. Field hockey sticks, with small curved ends, are much shorter than the long-bladed sticks used for ice hockey.

1. Regular lawn mowers are much _____ than push mowers.
   (A) quieter
   (B) simpler
   (C) noisier

2. How would you describe Adam and Joseph?
   (A) Very different
   (B) Very alike
   (C) Different in some ways but alike in others

3. What are two ways that downhill and cross-country skiing are similar?
   (A) Both sports take place on snow and use skis.
   (B) Both sports make skiers warm.
   (C) Both sports require fast strides to get down steep slopes.

4. How are the parks alike *and* different?
   (A) Both allow dogs, but the state park is larger.
   (B) Both are great parks, but families might like camping at the state park.
   (C) Both are wonderful places, but the national forest park has better facilities.

5. Ice hockey is different from field hockey in that
   (A) ice hockey uses six players, whereas field hockey uses eleven.
   (B) ice hockey sticks are much shorter than field hockey sticks.
   (C) ice hockey requires a player to hit an object into a goal, whereas field hockey does not.

6.   The redwood trees that grow along the California and Oregon coast are the largest trees in the world. These coastal redwood trees can reach heights of more than 350 feet. The trunks can measure more than 40 feet around. The trees are also among the oldest trees on Earth. Some of them are more than 2,000 years old.

---

7.   The trunks of the coastal redwoods are huge. Many years ago people made tunnels through the trunks of some redwoods. The people would charge visitors to drive through the tunnels in their cars. There are still redwoods with tunnels through which people can drive. However, now we know it is important to protect the trees. No one is allowed to make tunnels anymore.

---

8.   The redwoods that grow along the coast of California and Oregon are similar to pine trees in some ways. They are evergreen, just as pine trees are. That means their leaves stay green all year. They also produce cones that contain their seeds. The seeds of these redwoods are tiny. To get just one pound of seeds, you would need to collect about 125,000 of them.

---

9.   You would expect redwood trees to grow from redwood seeds. There are also other ways new redwood trees can start. New redwood trees can sprout from the stump of a redwood tree. Sometimes if a tree falls over, new trees will grow from the branches that are facing toward the sky.

---

10.   Redwood trees can be found in states such as Ohio and Florida, but they will never grow as big as the redwoods found along the coast of California and Oregon. The weather along the coast makes the difference. The fog that rolls in from the ocean provides the needed moisture. Also, the temperature along the coast stays at about 50 to 60 degrees Fahrenheit throughout the year.

6. Coastal redwood trees are
   (A) smaller in California than in Oregon.
   (B) the largest trees in the world.
   (C) larger in California than in Oregon.

---

7. Compared with years ago, redwoods
   (A) are protected more now.
   (B) are protected less now.
   (C) are not protected.

---

8. How are redwoods and pine trees alike?
   (A) They produce seed cones.
   (B) Their leaves turn red.
   (C) There are 125,000 trees of each kind.

---

9. New redwood trees can
   (A) start only from seeds.
   (B) sprout only from stumps.
   (C) start in different ways.

---

10. The weather along the coast of California and Oregon is
   (A) no different from the weather in Ohio.
   (B) different from the weather in Florida and Ohio.
   (C) the same as the weather in Florida.

1.   Blues music has been around for a long time. African work songs and spirituals formed the basis for this music that originated in the southern United States. Two types of blues music popular today are Delta blues and Chicago blues. Both Chicago and Delta blues feature simple, three-chord song structures that encourage blues singers and instrumentalists to improvise. Delta blues, however, is an older style of blues that showcases solo performers playing slide guitars. Chicago blues developed in the 1940s and 1950s when groups of musicians added electric guitars, drums, and keyboards to the sound.

2.   If you ever happen upon a legless lizard, you might think it is a snake. Both animals move without using external limbs, and both are cold-blooded reptiles that modify their behavior to control their body temperature. The two reptiles burrow underground and also have an acute sense of smell. Yet legless lizards contrast with snakes in enough ways to be considered lizards. Unlike snakes, legless lizards have ear openings and also movable eyelids. Snakes have forked tongues, but the tongues of legless lizards are pointed. Legless lizards also have rigid jaws, whereas snakes have flexible jaws that allow them to eat large prey.

3.   Looks can be deceiving. What do you think of when you hear the word **diamond?** A diamond is perhaps the hardest known substance on Earth. This clear, usually colorless mineral is also very expensive. Did you know that something we use every day has a great deal in common with diamonds? It is the dark, soft substance inside your pencil called graphite. It looks completely different from a diamond, yet chemists classify graphite as exactly the same element—carbon. Diamonds and graphite are ultimately dissimilar because of the differing amounts of heat and pressure put on each while they are forming.

4.   The weather station predicts both freezing rain and sleet. Is there really a difference between these two cold types of precipitation? Freezing rain is very cold rain that may start as snow, melt when it hits a section of warm air on its way down, and freeze after it hits a cold surface. Ice storms, in which a thin layer of ice forms on trees, are caused by rain that freezes on contact. Sleet is much rarer. The raindrops of sleet are already frozen and bounce when they hit a hard surface. Sleet occcurs on the coldest side of a warm front, farther away from the formation of freezing rain.

5.   Have you ever eaten a plantain? This long, thick-skinned fruit is closely related to the banana that many people are used to eating as a snack. If you were offered a plantain, you might be tempted to peel and eat it just like a banana. Yet bananas and plantains have some important differences. Plantains are the starchier of these two starchy fruits. They are hard to peel, and they taste good raw only when they turn dark. Plantains are used more often for cooking. Like baked potatoes, plantains are delicious when they are cooked and eaten right in their own skins.

ADVANCED TEST • COMPARING & CONTRASTING

1. How do the Chicago blues contrast with the Delta blues?
   (A) Only the Chicago blues feature improvisation.
   (B) The Chicago blues feature more musicians playing a variety of newer instruments.
   (C) Only the Chicago blues have simple, three-chord song structures.
   (D) The Chicago blues have been around for a longer period of time.

---

2. Which sentence best compares and contrasts the two reptiles?
   (A) Legless lizards have movable eyelids and rigid jaws, unlike snakes.
   (B) Both reptiles are cold-blooded and have a good sense of smell.
   (C) Both animals move without external limbs, but only snakes have flexible jaws.
   (D) Snakes have forked tongues, whereas those of legless lizards are pointed.

---

3. Why does it make sense to compare diamonds to graphite when they look so different?
   (A) Diamonds are hard, but graphite is very soft.
   (B) Graphite is really an unpolished diamond.
   (C) People like diamonds better than graphite.
   (D) Both diamonds and graphite are the common element known as carbon.

---

4. What is a key difference between freezing rain and sleet?
   (A) Freezing rain is liquid before it lands, whereas sleet is already frozen.
   (B) Freezing rain is colder than sleet.
   (C) Sleet falls more frequently than freezing rain.
   (D) Sleet never occurs during ice storms.

---

5. Which sentence best compares and contrasts plantains and bananas?
   (A) Bananas are easier to peel and enjoy raw.
   (B) Plantains are rarer than bananas but generally more healthful to eat.
   (C) Bananas and plantains are completely different fruits, but they look the same.
   (D) Bananas and plantains are closely related starchy fruits that are eaten differently.

6.   Many humans owe the ability to stay warm in winter to their feathered friends—birds. The fine, soft feathers underneath the outside feathers of adult birds, especially geese, are used for everything from bed comforters to jackets. Down is lightweight, resilient, and long-lasting, and it compresses. Many people consider it to be the best insulating fabric. One drawback to down is that it loses its insulating ability when it is wet. Synthetic insulating materials that have been produced are compressible, fluffy, and warm like down, but they insulate better when wet. They may be an advantage for people who are allergic to down.

7.   One of the most recognizable house cats is the Siamese. This slender, elegant-looking cat was recorded living in Thailand in the 1300s. It is known for its pale body with darker-hued points on its legs, feet, tail, and face. It has large ears on its triangular head and is somewhat vocal. Its quieter relative, the Balinese cat, is also slender and graceful. More recently bred, it is the result of pairing Siamese cats with Angora cats. Similar in coloring to Siamese cats, Balinese cats are often creamy with darker markings. Their fur is much longer, however, and they have somewhat bushy tails.

8.   Sit by a pond on a summer day and you may be delighted by shimmering, long-winged insects flitting about in search of mosquitoes and other edible insects. The long-winged insects are dragonflies and damselflies, known for their agility, swiftness, and excellent eyesight. They have a clever way of catching their food. During flight, they fold their legs into a netlike or basket configuration and collect their prey from the air. When they rest, you can see that the dragonfly has a larger abdomen and holds its wings straight out from its body. The slimmer damselfly holds its motionless wings together with the tips meeting over its back.

9.   Porpoises and dolphins have many similarities, and people often confuse these two aquatic mammals. Both are considered types of toothed whales. Like whales, they belong to the scientific order Cetacea. Both have a streamlined body, tail fluke, and a blowhole used for breathing. Yet these two animals belong to different families and are as physically different from one another as cats and dogs. Dolphins may grow to more than ten feet in length, while porpoises stay under seven feet. The bodies of dolphins are sleek. By contrast, porpoise bodies are wide. Dolphins have wave-shaped dorsal fins, and porpoises have triangle-shaped fins like sharks.

10.   The Alvaraz family discussed their options for traveling to Manhattan. If they drove, they could drive their car into the city and park. They could leave easily and could make a side trip to visit cousins in New Jersey. Another option was to take the train. At $60 per round-trip ticket, fares for the four of them would cost $240. Yet with gas and bridge and turnpike tolls, car travel would easily cost $100 or more. Parking would cost another $105 for the three nights they planned to stay. Driving was slightly cheaper, but the train would be more enjoyable and relaxing.

6. Which statement best contrasts artificial insulating fabric with down?
   (A) Synthetic insulating fabrics may cause allergies and do not compress as well.
   (B) Synthetic insulating materials are not quite as warm as down, but they insulate better when wet.
   (C) Synthetic insulating materials are warm, compressible, and lightweight like down.
   (D) Unlike down, synthetic materials are easy to find.

7. Which is *not* a point of comparison between Balinese and Siamese cats?
   (A) Siamese and Balinese cats have similar markings.
   (B) Both are pale in color.
   (C) Siamese and Balinese cats are equally vocal.
   (D) Siamese and Balinese cats are lean and graceful.

8. Which statement best compares *and* contrasts dragonflies and damselflies?
   (A) Both insects have excellent eyesight, but only the damselfly rests with its wing tips touching.
   (B) Neither insect is seen outdoors in cold weather.
   (C) The dragonfly is thicker in the abdomen, and it rests with its wings straight out.
   (D) Damselflies are slender in the abdomen and are quicker in flight.

9. Which best describes how porpoises and dolphins are different?
   (A) Porpoises and dolphins have very little in common.
   (B) Porpoises and dolphins have very few differences.
   (C) Porpoises have more in common with sharks than with dolphins.
   (D) Dolphins generally grow longer than porpoises and have a wave-shaped dorsal fin rather than a sharklike dorsal fin.

10. Which best describes how the Alvaraz family uses compare/contrast to make their decision?
    (A) By comparing both alternatives, they realized taking the train was a poor choice.
    (B) Contrasting the two travel alternatives allowed them to better weigh the differences.
    (C) By contrasting the two, they realized that driving was by far the superior way to travel.
    (D) After comparing the two, they realized that the costs would be exactly the same.

IDENTIFYING CAUSE & EFFECT

Special Instructions

1. Have students read the entire passage. Remind them to be aware of what happens in the passage and why it happens. Review the clue words that might be included in the passage that will help students determine whether something is a cause or an effect. The words *because, for this reason,* and *since* signal a cause. Words such as *so, consequently,* and *as a result* signal an effect.

2. After completing the passage, students should read the questions and choose the correct answer to each.

Answer Sheet Blackline Masters for tests in this skill strand:

    Primary Test: Use Answer Sheet 3.

    Intermediate Test: Use Answer Sheet 4.

    Advanced Test: Use Answer Sheet 4.

PLACEMENT TABLE

	Raw Score (Number Correct)	Book Placement
Primary Test	0–1	Picture
	2	Preparatory
	3–4	A
	5–6	B
	7–8	C
Intermediate Test	3–4	D
	5–7	E
	8–10	F
Advanced Test	5–7	G
	8–10	H

Ella was sad. She had planted a seed in her garden a few days ago. So far, nothing had grown. When she told her mother about the seed, her mother said, "You need to keep watering the seed, Ella. Otherwise, it will not grow."

Ella watered the garden every day. A few days later, she saw something in the dirt. It was a little plant!

1. Why did the seed grow?
   (A) Ella put more dirt on it.
   (B) Ella sang to it.
   (C) Ella watered it.

David played with his dog outside. He threw a ball. The dog chased it under the tree. A cat was hiding under the tree. The cat ran across the yard. The dog ran after the cat. David ran after his dog.

2. Why did David chase his dog?
   (A) David threw a ball.
   (B) His dog chased a cat.
   (C) They were outside.

Grandpa gave Justin a rubber ball for his birthday. They went outside to play catch. Justin threw the ball at Grandpa. The ball sailed over his head. The ball hit a glass of water on the picnic table. Grandpa and Justin went to find a broom.

3. Why did Grandpa and Justin need to find a broom?
   (A) The ball broke the picnic table.
   (B) The ball broke a window.
   (C) The ball broke the glass.

One day the Smith family had a picnic in the park. They set out dishes of food and then sat down to eat. Soon the clouds grew dark. A bright flash of light crossed the sky. The family grabbed their plates and ran to their car.

4. What caused the picnic to end?
   (A) The family sat down to eat.
   (B) A storm blew in.
   (C) The family ran to their car.

5. Emily was in her room. She heard a loud noise. "What was that?" she asked. Then there was another sound. Her cat jumped. It ran away from her. Emily saw the broken glass on the floor. "Now I know."

---

6. One night there was a very loud storm. The wind blew. Rain fell all night. The next morning Darnell saw a big tree branch on the ground. "It fell right outside our house," he told his father. "Why didn't I hear it?"

---

7. Mr. Reed went to the play. He left his coat in the coatroom. When the play was over, Mr. Reed put on his coat. It did not fit. His keys were not in his pocket. Just then he heard a man say, "Why do I have keys in my pocket?"

---

8. There was going to be a big race. The first prize was ten dollars. The second prize was five dollars. The third prize was three dollars. Sue ran in the race. When it was over, Sue got five dollars.

5. Why did the cat run out of the room?
 (A) The cat made a sound.
 (B) The cat broke the glass.
 (C) The cat wants to see Emily.

---

6. Why didn't Darnell hear the tree fall?
 (A) The storm was too loud.
 (B) Darnell was too loud.
 (C) It was dark.

---

7. Why didn't the coat fit Mr. Reed?
 (A) He ate too much.
 (B) He left it in the coatroom.
 (C) He was wearing the wrong coat.

---

8. Why did Sue get five dollars?
 (A) She won the race.
 (B) She won second prize.
 (C) She liked prizes.

1.   Nate knew he should act quickly. The aquarium filter was clogged again, causing green algae to grow on the sides of the aquarium. This same effect occurred last week when the filter clogged. Nate worked to clean the tank and unclog the filter because he knew his fish would be healthier in clear water.

---

2.   Mrs. Romero's class was excited. This was the first month they won. They earned more bonus points than any other class because everybody turned in their reading logs and because they were the quietest class in the cafeteria. The principal gave them two extra recesses.

---

3.   Every year when the third weekend in June rolled around, Ellie felt the excitement build. All her neighbors made sure they were home for the Burlington Bicycle Race. Because the finish line was on her street, people gathered there to picnic and cheer the racers.

---

4.   When José and Chris saw dark storm clouds, they hoped it would not thunder. They had just arrived at the pool. When they were in the middle of a water polo game, they heard a deep rumble. The lifeguard blew her whistle and made an announcement. They had to climb out of the pool.

---

5.   "Our cat Felicity is in trouble with my parents again. She scratched the sofa," said Mira.
    "Why don't you make her a scratching post?" asked Jenna. "Our cat used to scratch our furniture, so we built her a carpeted post. Now she leaves the furniture alone."

INTERMEDIATE TEST • IDENTIFYING CAUSE & EFFECT

1. What caused green algae to grow on the sides of the aquarium?
   (A) The fish were becoming unhealthy.
   (B) The aquarium filter was clogged.
   (C) Nick never cleaned the aquarium.

2. What was the effect of earning the most bonus points?
   (A) Mrs. Romero's class had to be quieter the next month.
   (B) The class received extra reading time.
   (C) The class received two extra recesses.

3. Which was *not* an effect of the Burlington Bicycle Race?
   (A) Neighbors picnicked on their lawns.
   (B) Neighbors kept people off their lawns.
   (C) The excitement built in Ellie's neighborhood.

4. Which is an example of a cause leading to an effect in this paragraph?
   (A) The lifeguard blew her whistle and it thundered.
   (B) The water polo game caused the deep rumble.
   (C) José and Chris saw dark storm clouds and hoped it would not thunder.

5. What does Jenna believe caused her cat to stop scratching furniture?
   (A) Her family made a carpeted post for the cat.
   (B) Her parents reprimanded the cat.
   (C) The cat no longer likes to scratch.

6.   Before 1848 California was part of Mexico. When John Sutter came to California in 1839, he asked the Mexican governor of California to give him 50,000 acres of land. Before getting the land, Sutter had to become a citizen of Mexico. After Sutter got his land, he began to clear it and build a fort. Most people called the land Sutter's Fort.

7.   John Sutter wanted to build a sawmill to make lumber. James Marshall helped Sutter build the mill. Marshall had to find land that was near water because water was needed to turn the mill wheel. He also wanted to find a place where there were many trees to use to make lumber. Marshall chose a place by a river near Sutter's Fort.

8.   James Marshall hired workers to build the sawmill. The workers also built a kind of track, called a *race,* to send water to the mill wheel. On January 24, 1848, Marshall was examining the race when he noticed some shiny gold rocks in the water. He walked right into the water and bent down to pick up the rocks.

9.   Marshall tested the rocks to see if they were gold. After he was sure that they were gold, he rode off to tell John Sutter. The men tried to keep the discovery of gold quiet. They knew that if word got out, many people would come from all over to try to find gold. The gold seekers would ruin the fields and dig up the land.

10.   Keeping the discovery of gold a secret was impossible. People told one another about the discovery. Soon a small article appeared in a California newspaper. The word spread across the country. People across the country came to California to find gold. Some even came from around the world. The California gold rush had begun.

6. Sutter became a Mexican citizen because
   (A) he wanted to get land.
   (B) he moved to California.
   (C) he knew the Mexican governor.

7. James Marshall chose a place near the river because
   (A) trees grew in the river.
   (B) water was needed to run the mill.
   (C) a sawmill was already there.

8. Marshall picked up the rocks because
   (A) they were in the water.
   (B) they looked like gold.
   (C) he walked into the water.

9. Marshall tested the rocks because he wanted to
   (A) keep the gold for himself.
   (B) keep the discovery quiet.
   (C) see if they were gold.

10. People came to California to
   (A) settle there.
   (B) tell one another about the discovery.
   (C) find gold.

ADVANCED TEST • IDENTIFYING CAUSE & EFFECT

1. It crawls across land. It is a voracious eater of native fish and small mammals. It could be the most dangerous fish introduced to North American waters, and it could be coming to a lake near you. This unusual fish from Asia, called the snakehead, is turning up in various rivers and lakes. Snakeheads likely found their way here after being sold as pets or as delicacies in specialty fish markets. When a non-native species is released into an ecosystem other than its own, it can throw the local ecosystem out of balance. Through competition or by preying on native species, it can threaten the survival of native plants and animals.

2. Jeff and Aimee run a community-supported farm where they produce vegetables and fruit for 120 families. Last summer they experienced a long drought that caused many of their crops to suffer. They were thrilled when they had steady rain throughout the following spring. But the rain kept falling, continuing through most of the summer. Sunshine came intermittently, but on the balance they had too much rain. The cucumbers, beets, carrots, and raspberries did well in these conditions, but the tomatoes did not fare so well. Because the tomatoes were drenched day after day and then exposed to sun, their skins cracked and their blossoms rotted.

3. Americans today spend a lot of time washing, but their pursuit of cleanliness pales in comparison to the ancient Romans. Dry skin and dry hair were considered dirty by the ancient Romans, so they bathed and moisturized more than once a day. What they used for bathing is even more interesting—olive oil. People bathed with olive oil at least three times daily or coated themselves with it and skimmed the excess off with a stick called a *strigel*. In order to protect their skin from dirt and cold, they left a thin film of oil on their bodies.

4. When the Rojas' new collie Ranger began shedding more than usual in May, it didn't surprise them. They figured he was getting rid of his winter coat in preparation for the warm summer weather. When he began shedding again that fall, they were puzzled until they spoke with their veterinarian. She told them that some breeds, such as shelties and collies, are double coated. They have a tough protective overcoat as well as a soft insulating undercoat. They lose large quantities of fur during the spring and during the fall when they change their coat for the new season.

5. The pupil is the opening, which expands and contracts, in the center of the iris in your eye. The pupil acts like the eye's window, and it is the only place where light enters. If you were to look into a friend's eyes in a bright light and then in darkness, you would notice his or her dark pupils quickly expanding to let in more light for seeing. The lighter-colored iris around the pupil is actually a circular muscle that adjusts the pupil. When pupils expand and contract, they regulate the amount of light, so a fixed amount enters the eyes regardless of the light intensity.

ADVANCED TEST • IDENTIFYING CAUSE & EFFECT

1. What would be the most likely negative effect of too many snakehead fish living in North American waters?
   (A) Snakeheads could be sold as pets or for food.
   (B) Snakeheads could travel over land to people's yards.
   (C) Snakehead fish could threaten the survival of native species of fish.
   (D) Snakeheads could become extinct in Asia.

2. What was *not* an effect of too much rain at the community-supported farm?
   (A) Some carrots thrived, but the raspberries rotted on the bushes.
   (B) The skins of the tomatoes ended up cracking.
   (C) The beets and carrots were a success.
   (D) The tomatoes had blossom end rot.

3. What did *not* cause the Romans to bathe with olive oil?
   (A) They believed oil protected the skin from cold.
   (B) The Romans believed dry skin and hair was unclean.
   (C) They did not have enough water for bathing.
   (D) They believed a layer of olive oil could protect them from dirt.

4. Which is an example of a cause leading to an effect in this paragraph?
   (A) Ranger shed in the fall because he needed a different type of coat for colder weather.
   (B) Ranger was a new dog and as a result shed in both the spring and fall.
   (C) After looking over Ranger, the veterinarian helped him stop shedding.
   (D) The Rojas gave Ranger a warm coat for the winter.

5. What could cause a pupil to shrink, expand, and shrink again?
   (A) Exposure to darkness, light, and then darkness again
   (B) Exposure to increasingly brighter light
   (C) Exposure to light, darkness, and then light again
   (D) Exposure to steadily decreasing light

6.   You can tell the age of a male deer by counting the number of points on its antlers. A young buck of eighteen months will have a smaller rack of antlers, but the number of points will be the same as those of a mature four-year-old. Both bucks are likely to have eight points. A five- to six-year-old buck is likely to have the widest rack of all, with eight points or more. A buck's rack size and width are determined most by diet and, to a lesser degree, genetics. Deer that eat healthy foods are most likely to grow large racks of antlers.

7.   The bubonic plague of the 1300s, also known as the black plague, was perhaps the most deadly disease in history. It killed almost one-third of Europe's population. People at the time had a poor understanding of its cause. Some people believed poisoned well water was the cause or that the plague was a punishment. A better understanding of the disease would have helped them escape or combat it. Scientists who studied the plague later surmised that tiny fleas carried by mice and black rats spread the deadly virus. As winter arrived, rodents looking for warmth moved into people's homes. Biting fleas could infect an entire family and cause a new outbreak.

8.   Have you ever thought of a forest or field as a sponge? Acres of soil rich with plants and natural matter absorb and filter excess water from rain and snow. What happens when a forest or field is replaced with parking lots, houses, and stores? These hard, impervious surfaces do not absorb water so readily. Instead, a large volume of water known as runoff flows from compacted lawns, rooftops, and driveways. This runoff carries pesticides, motor oil, and other chemicals to nearby streams and rivers. According to government estimates, a city block generates nine times more runoff than a woodland area of the same size.

9.   The Kellermans' favorite restaurant used to be Hamburger Haven. Everybody in the family loved the food. From fish tacos to veggie wraps to classic hamburgers, Hamburger Haven had something for everyone, and it was inexpensive. Another of its advantages was that the Kellermans never had to wait for a seat. Then a major newspaper of a nearby city praised Hamburger Haven in a restaurant review. Things changed at the restaurant. Long lines began forming out the door, and prices slowly inched up. The Kellermans rarely went to Hamburger Haven anymore. They began looking for a new favorite restaurant.

10.   If you live where it gets very cold during winter, you may have seen houses with collections of long, pointed icicles. These intriguing, icy formations occur when warm air under the roof (such as in an attic) causes snow on the rooftop to melt. As melting snow flows down the roof, it reaches the colder surface of the roof hanging over the eaves. If this surface is below 32 degrees, it begins to freeze. Often drops of melted snow dribble off the roof, hit the cold air, and freeze as ice. The icicle grows layer by layer as more drops melt and freeze.

6. What would be the most likely cause of a six-year-old buck having a small rack of antlers?
- **(A)** The buck is too young to have a large rack.
- **(B)** The buck has been in fights with other bucks.
- **(C)** The buck is not getting good nutrition.
- **(D)** The buck lost its large antlers.

---

7. What was the effect of ignorance about the cause of the black plague?
- **(A)** People used the plague to punish others.
- **(B)** People were not equipped to fight or avoid it.
- **(C)** People began exterminating rodents and fleas.
- **(D)** People welcomed rodents into their homes.

---

8. Based on the paragraph, which cause could lead to the effect(s) described?
- **(A)** When land is paved, storms are more likely to occur.
- **(B)** As forests and fields are paved, streams and rivers dry up.
- **(C)** When impervious surfaces are constructed, people use fewer chemicals.
- **(D)** Paved surfaces may result in excess runoff that pollutes streams.

---

9. What would have been the likely effect of a negative article about Hamburger Haven?
- **(A)** Hamburger Haven would immediately close so nobody could eat there.
- **(B)** The Kellermans would start a letter-writing campaign complaining to the newspaper.
- **(C)** Hamburger Haven would not have a large menu.
- **(D)** Hamburger Haven would open a second restaurant.

---

10. Which is *not* among the causes leading to the formation of icicles?
- **(A)** Warm air is present under a rooftop covered with snow.
- **(B)** Snow melts and flows to a colder section of the roof.
- **(C)** Water dripping off the roof freezes in layers.
- **(D)** People see icicles hanging from the eaves of some houses.

IDENTIFYING FACT & OPINION

Special Instructions

1. Students should read the entire passage slowly, keeping in mind the difference between a fact and an opinion. Remind students that a fact is true and can be proven. An opinion is a feeling or belief. Sometimes opinions begin with clue words such as *I believe, I think,* or *in my opinion.*

2. After reading the passage, students should read the questions and choose the correct answer to each.

Answer Sheet Blackline Masters for tests in this skill strand:

    Primary Test: Use Answer Sheet 3.

    Intermediate Test: Use Answer Sheet 4.

    Advanced Test: Use Answer Sheet 4.

PLACEMENT TABLE

	Raw Score (Number Correct)	Book Placement
Primary Test	0–1	Picture
	2	Preparatory
	3–4	A
	5–6	B
	7–8	C
Intermediate Test	3–4	D
	5–7	E
	8–10	F
Advanced Test	5–7	G
	8–10	H

Doris cleaned the house for her father. He gave her some money for working. The next day, Doris could not find her money. Then she found it. It was in her shoe!

1. Which sentence tells a fact?

   (A) Cleaning is hard work.

   (B) A shoe is a good place to hide money.

   (C) Doris found the money in her shoe.

Dante read a story to the class. Everybody thought the story was funny. Suddenly Dante's cat walked into the classroom. The class laughed even more when the cat sat down to listen.

2. Which sentence tells an opinion?

   (A) Dante is a good reader.

   (B) Dante's cat walked into the classroom.

   (C) The class laughed when the cat sat down.

"I will go to bed soon," said Nancy. "I want to read this story first." Her mother and father went to bed. The next day, her mother found Nancy sleeping in the chair. She had gone to sleep reading the story.

3. It is a fact that

   (A) reading will always make you sleepy.

   (B) Nancy fell asleep in the chair.

   (C) reading is exciting.

___

When Mr. and Mrs. Champlin had a baby, they didn't know what to name her. Then Mr. Champlin said, "Remember when we went to Florence on vacation? It was a pretty city. Let's call our daughter Florence."

4. It is an opinion that

   (A) Mr. and Mrs. Champlin had a baby.

   (B) Mr. and Mrs. Champlin went on vacation.

   (C) Florence is a pretty city.

5.   Hamsters make the best pets. They are small and do not eat a lot of food. You can pick them up because they are soft and cuddly. They need only a small cage, a wheel to run on, food, and water. Even if you have no yard, you can have a hamster as a pet.

---

6.   John likes to eat cookies because they taste good. His mother makes them every Saturday. She makes sugar cookies. John helps her make them. He licks the spoon. John thinks his mother makes the best cookies in the world!

---

7.   New York City is a great place to live. It is one of the biggest cities in the world. Many people live in New York. It has very tall buildings and sits beside the ocean. You don't have to have a car if you live in New York. It has subways that go under the ground and buses that go down the streets. It is a pretty city, and there is a lot to do there!

---

8.   Ellen thought her sister did everything right. Her sister got good grades in school. She had a lot of friends. Ellen's sister was a great dancer. She sang well. She had good manners and was nice to everyone. Ellen thought her sister was great.

5. It is a fact that

    (A) hamsters make the best pets.

    (B) hamsters are cuddly.

    (C) hamsters need food.

---

6. It is an opinion that

    (A) John's mother makes cookies every Saturday.

    (B) John's mother makes sugar cookies.

    (C) John's mother makes the best cookies in the world.

---

7. It is a fact that

    (A) New York City sits near the ocean.

    (B) New York City is a pretty city.

    (C) New York City is a great place to live.

---

8. It is an opinion that Ellen's sister

    (A) has a lot of friends.

    (B) gets good grades.

    (C) does everything right.

1.   Lakes are found all over the world for different reasons. However, glaciers carved out most of them in North America. Nearly half of the world's lakes are located in Canada. Glaciers also created the Great Lakes and most of Minnesota's many lakes. The areas carved out by the glaciers filled with water. A lake is a beautiful sight, no matter how it was formed.

2.   Americans are annoyed with one-dollar coins. The three that have been minted since 1970 have been unpopular with both store clerks and customers, but they shouldn't be so picky. A one-dollar coin is more costly to produce than a dollar bill. However, it will last about 30 years longer.

3.   The thought of eating insects turns most people's stomachs. Yet insects are used for food in some parts of the world. They are very high in protein. As the world population grows, it might be hard to feed everyone. Insects may someday be needed as an important source of food.

4.   When the Plains Indians hunted buffalo, they carried their tepees with them. Tepees were made and owned by the women of a tribe. Women also put them up and took them down. All tepee doorways had to face east toward the rising sun. Tepees were also decorated beautifully.

5.   The hippopotamus is a strange-looking animal. It is as big around as it is long. It has short, heavy legs and a huge head supported by a thick neck. A hippo weighs between 3,000 and 7,000 pounds or more. Coated with mud, the hippo is not a pretty sight.

1. Which sentence is an opinion?
   (A) A lake is a beautiful sight, no matter how it was formed.
   (B) Nearly half of the world's lakes are located in Canada.
   (C) Glaciers also created the Great Lakes and most of Minnesota's many lakes.

---

2. Which sentence is a fact?
   (A) Americans are annoyed with one-dollar coins.
   (B) A one-dollar coin is more costly to produce than a dollar bill.
   (C) Americans shouldn't be so picky.

---

3. Which sentence is based on an opinion?
   (A) Insects are very high in protein.
   (B) Insects are used for food in some parts of the world
   (C) The thought of eating insects turns most people's stomachs.

---

4. Which sentence is an opinion?
   (A) All tepee doorways had to face east toward the rising sun.
   (B) Tepees were made and owned by the women of a tribe.
   (C) Tepees were decorated beautifully.

---

5. Which sentence is a fact?
   (A) The hippopotamus is a strange-looking animal.
   (B) A hippo weighs between 3,000 and 7,000 pounds or more.
   (C) Coated with mud, the hippo is not a pretty sight.

6.   In 1896 there was no house made of ice that was equal to the Ice Palace in Leadville, Colorado. The Ice Palace in Leadville was as big as ten football fields. It cost $60,000 to build and had walls eight feet thick! Inside were a skating rink, a restaurant, and two dance halls.

---

7.   The squirrel is lucky to have a long tail. The tail is useful for many different purposes. When the sun gets hot, the squirrel holds its tail above its head like an umbrella. In the cold, the squirrel uses its tail as a warm blanket. The most important use for its tail is balance.

---

8.   For Tia Hunnicut, her dolls meant business. She didn't play with them. She made them! Tia started constructing dolls when she was thirteen. Tia designed the dolls' clothing, painted their faces, and put the pieces together. Tia's business, called Tia's Doll Emporium, grew so large that she hired three people to help her.

---

9.   Clown College is where students learn to be circus clowns. Only about fifty students of the thousands who try out are chosen. They go to school from 8:30 in the morning until 10:00 at night for eight weeks. They learn to tumble, walk a high wire, run on stilts, and paint their faces.

---

10.   Weighing up to three hundred pounds and growing to twelve feet in length, Komodo dragons take their name from their home, Komodo Island, in the western Pacific Ocean. A pilot discovered them after making a forced landing there. A museum sent scientists to the island. They took pictures and brought back dragons for the museum.

6. Which statement is an opinion?

(A) The Ice Palace was as big as ten football fields.

(B) The Ice Palace was a fun place to go as a family.

(C) The Ice Palace had walls eight feet thick.

---

7. It is a fact that

(A) the most important use of a squirrel's tail is for balance.

(B) the squirrel is lucky to have a long tail.

(C) when the sun is hot, the squirrel holds its tail above its head.

---

8. It is an opinion that

(A) Tia's business is called Tia's Doll Emporium.

(B) Tia started constructing dolls when she was thirteen years old.

(C) Tia's doll business is fun.

---

9. Which statement is a fact?

(A) Only fifty students of the thousands who try out for Clown College are chosen.

(B) Walking a high wire is the hardest skill a clown can learn.

(C) Working until 10:00 P.M. is too much.

---

10. It is an opinion that

(A) the Komodo dragon is a frightening creature.

(B) Komodo Island is located in the Pacific Ocean.

(C) scientists brought Komodo dragons back to the museum.

ADVANCED TEST • IDENTIFYING FACT & OPINION

1.   The baby's face that has probably been seen by more people than any other in the world is the face found on products made by a well-known baby food company. The label, with the cute baby's face, first appeared on the market in 1928. For years many people claimed to have been the model for the picture, and it was even rumored to be the face of the late movie actor Humphrey Bogart. Finally in 1951, Ann Cook settled the question. A close friend of Ann's parents, Dorothy Hope Smith, had drawn Ann's face when Ann was four months old. The baby food company began using it almost immediately. It was twenty-three years later that Ann went to the company with proof that she had been the true model.

2.   The woolly mammoth's teeth played an important role in its survival. It had large, curved tusks, which were often very elaborate and beautiful. Tusks are, in fact, enlarged and specialized teeth. The woolly mammoth used them to clear snow from food sources and as protection from predators. The woolly mammoth's molars were also specialized. They were well suited for grazing on tough tundra vegetation. The molars had a layer of ridges, which were ideal for grinding coarse grasses. Woolly mammoths also had four molars throughout their lifetime. When these molars wore down, they fell out. Then a new set of molars grew in. Each mammoth had six sets of replacement teeth.

3.   Visiting Colonial Williamsburg today is like stepping back in time. There it seems that the year is still 1774. The American Revolution is just about to begin. Virginia is England's largest and wealthiest colony. It is also thought of as England's most loyal colony. Many Virginians were once proud of this, but some are beginning to feel differently. England keeps increasing their taxes. Many colonists think this is unfair. Williamsburg became a main gathering place for colonists who opposed English rule.

4.   Can you imagine a world without paper? The invention of paper was a momentous occasion. Its most basic use is for writing or drawing, but we also use it for wrapping, packaging, toweling, clothing, food serving, and more. We use paper so frequently that it is hard to believe there was a time when it did not exist. Scholars believe the inventor was an Egyptian living about five thousand years ago. Egyptian paper was called papyrus. It was a kind of thin mat made of grasses that had been pounded together and then dried. Records, art, and religious texts were kept on papyrus.

5.   Zoos have existed since ancient times. Records show that people in the Middle East kept aviaries more than 7,000 years ago. Records also show that wealthy ancient Egyptians kept wild animals in beautiful gardens. What might have been the first public zoo was in China. The emperor Wen Wang introduced it about 3,000 years ago. He called it the Garden of Intelligence. Chinese scholars went there to study animals and exchange information about them. Interest in wild and exotic animals has not lessened over the years. Most of today's cities have a zoo, a wildlife park, or an aquarium, which contains hundreds of different animals. They are studied and observed by both the public and researchers.

ADVANCED TEST • IDENTIFYING FACT & OPINION

1. It is a fact that
   (A) the baby on the baby food label looked like Humphrey Bogart.
   (B) the baby on the baby food label had a cute face.
   (C) many people claimed to have been the model for the baby food label.
   (D) the baby's face on the baby food label is the most popular face in the world.

2. It is an opinion that
   (A) the woolly mammoth's tusks were elaborate and beautiful.
   (B) the woolly mammoth had tusks.
   (C) the woolly mammoth's molars had a layer of ridges.
   (D) each woolly mammoth had six sets of replacement teeth.

3. Which statement is a fact?
   (A) Visiting Colonial Williamsburg today is like stepping back in time.
   (B) Raising taxes is unfair.
   (C) Williamsburg became a gathering place for colonists who opposed English rule.
   (D) Colonial Williamsburg is thought of as England's most loyal colony.

4. Which statement is an opinion?
   (A) Egyptian paper was called papyrus
   (B) Papyrus was a kind of thin mat made of grasses that had been pounded together.
   (C) We use paper so frequently that it is hard to believe there was a time when it did not exist.
   (D) Records, art, and religious texts were kept on papyrus.

5. It is an opinion that
   (A) zoos have existed since ancient times.
   (B) the first public zoo in China was called the Garden of Intelligence.
   (C) people in the Middle East kept aviaries more than 7,000 years ago.
   (D) an aquarium is more interesting than an aviary.

6.   Ira Aldridge is regarded by many as the greatest Shakespearean actor of his time. Although he was born and educated in America, Ira learned that African American actors were more readily accepted overseas in the 1830s. In England he got a starring role as Othello, the Moor of Venice. He was so outstanding in the role that he was soon playing other leads such as Macbeth and Shylock. His fame spread over Europe. One man in the audience got so excited when Othello was supposed to be killing his wife that he jumped up and said that she was innocent.

7.   A wedding in the Philippines has many unique features. The festivities begin when friends of the bride and groom meet at the bride's house the day before the wedding. People bring pigs, chickens, fruits, and vegetables for the wedding party. They build a *pala-pala,* a tent with a roof of palm leaves and bamboo supports. At one end is a kitchen. The rest is used for eating and dancing. The highlight of the festivities is a dance that the newlyweds perform. As they dance, relatives pin money and even deeds to property on their clothes. Everyone has a good time, and the bride and groom receive many presents.

8.   For years Wilbert Bonvillain worked for the Southern Pacific Railroad. Later he ran a truck company. After he retired Bonvillain made wooden toys of all kinds— trucks, cats, dogs, sailboats, and airplanes. He made more than 22,000 wonderful toys. What did Bonvillain do with them? Some people urged him to sell them in stores, but Bonvillain gave the toys away to his grandchildren and to children in the neighborhood. Most of all, though, he liked to send the toys to schools, hospitals, and charities. Bonvillain said that his new "work" made him happier than ever before. The children who received his toys likely felt the same way.

9.   Pikes Peak is probably the best-known mountain in the Rocky Mountains. It reaches 14,110 feet above sea level. If you think that it is named after Zebulon Pike because he was the first to climb it, you're wrong! Zebulon Pike never reached the top. In 1806 Pike and some other explorers were journeying west and spotted the mountain about 100 miles away. Pike thought it would be easy to climb. He and three others decided to try it. They returned three days later, hungry and nearly frozen. Pike believed that no one could ever climb that mountain. Since that time many people have climbed it. Today you can drive, ride on horseback, or even take a nine-mile railway to the top. The mountain was named Pikes Peak because Zebulon Pike discovered it, not because he climbed it.

10.   Sharks are some of the strangest and most feared creatures in the sea. A few surprising facts about the fiercest of all sharks, the great white shark, might interest you. Great white sharks are not very good hunters at all. In fact, they are quite clumsy. They depend on their ability to sneak up on their next meal. However, seals, sea lions, and most fish usually avoid these giant sharks quite easily. But sharks do have razorlike teeth. What's more, they have two rows of teeth, with an unlimited supply of replacement teeth. If a shark loses a tooth, another one just moves into its place.

6. It is a fact that
   (A) Ira Aldridge was the best actor of his time.
   (B) Ira Aldridge was outstanding in the role of Othello.
   (C) Ira Aldridge was a Shakespearean actor.
   (D) Ira Aldridge was exciting as Othello.

7. It is an opinion that
   (A) everyone at Filipino weddings has a good time.
   (B) a *pala-pala* is a type of tent.
   (C) people eat and dance at weddings.
   (D) Filipino newlyweds often receive money as gifts.

8. It is an opinion that
   (A) Bonvillain made toys for his grandchildren.
   (B) Wilbert Bonvillain worked for the Southern Pacific Railroad.
   (C) Bonvillain made more than 22,000 toys.
   (D) Bonvillain's toys were wonderful.

9. Choose the statement that is an opinion.
   (A) Pikes Peak reaches 14,110 feet above sea level.
   (B) Pikes Peak is easy to climb.
   (C) Many people have climbed Pikes Peak since 1806.
   (D) Zebulon Pike was not the first person to climb Pikes Peak.

10. It is a fact that
   (A) sharks are the most feared creatures in the sea.
   (B) sharks have an unlimited supply of replacement teeth.
   (C) sharks are the strangest creatures in the sea.
   (D) all facts about sharks are surprising.

DRAWING CONCLUSIONS

Special Instructions

After reading each passage, students should select the correct answer. They must be made aware that, though several answers for a question might be true, the one correct answer must be supported by evidence from the paragraph. Answer choices are located below the passage in Exercises 1–4 of the Primary Test and on the opposite page thereafter.

Answer Sheet Blackline Masters for tests in this skill strand:

Primary Test: Use Answer Sheet 3.

Intermediate Test: Use Answer Sheet 4.

Advanced Test: Use Answer Sheet 4.

PLACEMENT TABLE

	Raw Score (Number Correct)	Book Placement
Primary Test	0–1	Picture
	2	Preparatory
	3–4	A
	5–6	B
	7–8	C
Intermediate Test	3–4	D
	5–7	E
	8–10	F
Advanced Test	5–7	G
	8–10	H

Mrs. Johnson took her class on a field trip. They visited Mr. Smith's farm. On the farm, the class saw cows, chickens, and pigs. The class said they wanted to come back next year.

1. From the story you can tell that
  (A) the class liked Mr. Smith's farm.
  (B) Mrs. Johnson knows Mr. Smith.
  (C) Mr. Smith had many cows.

Horatio fished every day. He always took his dog with him. Sometimes Horatio fished all morning without catching anything. That was all right with Horatio. He liked spending time with his dog.

2. From the story you can tell that
  (A) Horatio catches many fish.
  (B) the dog does not like water.
  (C) Horatio likes to fish.

Ira asked his dad if he had a pet when he was a little boy. His dad said, "Yes. My pet was a pretty yellow bird. The bird liked to sing. I miss that bird very much."

3. From the story you can tell that

(A) the bird was a canary.

(B) Ira's dad liked the bird.

(C) the bird lived in a cage.

"Will you water my houseplants when I go away?" asked Mr. Cruz. "I will pay you." Luis said he would water the plants. When Mr. Cruz got back, he saw how good his plants looked. "I should go away again," Mr. Cruz said. "The plants look better when Luis takes care of them."

4. From the story you can tell that

(A) Luis is good at taking care of plants.

(B) Mr. Cruz goes on many trips.

(C) Mr. Cruz paid Luis a lot of money.

5.   Emma won a ribbon at her school's field day last spring. The boys and girls ran races. They tried to see how far each of them could jump. Mr. Kwan gave ribbons to the winner of each contest.

---

6.   Coach Price showed the players how to hold the bat. She showed them how to swing it to get a hit. The pitcher threw the first ball to Eli. Before he knew it, the coach was yelling, "Run, Eli!"

---

7.   Jim wanted to go ice-skating. His grandmother said she would take him to the rink after he did his chores. "I didn't know you could work so fast!" said his grandmother.

---

8.   The soccer ball flew into the net. The goalie could not stop it. Marta and Anna jumped up and down. "Three to two," they cheered. "Now our coach should be smiling."

5. Why did Mr. Kwan give Emma a ribbon?

   (A) Emma always wanted a ribbon.

   (B) Emma won a contest.

   (C) Emma went to the field day.

---

6. Why did the coach tell Eli to run?

   (A) Eli got ready to hit the ball.

   (B) The pitcher was not very good.

   (C) Eli hit the ball.

---

7. Why did Jim work so fast?

   (A) His grandmother told him to.

   (B) He wanted to go ice-skating.

   (C) He wanted to get paid.

---

8. Why did Marta and Anna jump up and down?

   (A) Their team was winning.

   (B) They wanted the game to be over.

   (C) They wanted to stop the ball.

INTERMEDIATE TEST • DRAWING CONCLUSIONS

1.   Jan had a pet squirrel. One day the squirrel crawled into Jan's tuba and wouldn't come out. Jan tried everything to try to get her pet to come out of the horn. When nothing worked, Jan's father took the tuba with the squirrel in it to the veterinarian. The vet held five walnuts near the horn. Soon the squirrel crawled out of the tuba looking for the walnuts.

---

2.   Mrs. Steel couldn't find her expensive necklace. Her dog was the only one in the room. Mrs. Steel thought, "Maybe Scamp ate it!" She took Scamp to a hospital. An X-ray showed the necklace in Scamp's stomach. The necklace was safely removed with a special tool. The dog and the necklace were fine.

---

3.   Look at a dollar bill. The back of the bill shows a pyramid with thirteen steps. There are two Latin words with a total of thirteen letters. An eagle is shown carrying thirteen arrows and a branch with thirteen leaves. The eagle's shield has thirteen stripes. Thirteen stars are over its head.

---

4.   The tallest animal in the world is the giraffe. Giraffes are found in certain areas of Africa. The average height of a giraffe is eighteen feet. The tallest giraffe ever known stood nineteen feet tall—from the top of its head to the ground.

---

5.   Every whistle blow of a train has a different meaning. A number of short toots is a warning to people or animals on the track. A long whistle means that the train is nearing a station or a railroad crossing. Three short toots mean that the train is going to back up or stop.

1. You can tell that
   (A) Jan was angry.
   (B) Jan did not like the tuba.
   (C) Jan was worried.

---

2. You can tell that
   (A) Mrs. Steel doesn't like jewelry.
   (B) Scamp will eat odd things sometimes.
   (C) Mrs. Steel didn't want her jewelry back.

---

3. You can tell that
   (A) the one-dollar bill has many thirteens on it.
   (B) nobody speaks Latin anymore.
   (C) a five-dollar bill has more thirteens on it.

---

4. You can tell that
   (A) the giraffe is a ferocious animal.
   (B) the giraffe is taller than a person.
   (C) the giraffe can run fast.

---

5. You can tell that
   (A) to know the meaning of a train whistle, you need to hear it.
   (B) to know the meaning of a train whistle, you need to taste it.
   (C) to know the meaning of a train whistle, you need to touch it.

6.   The king of Bijapur was sick and would do anything to get well. A sneaky man told the king that if he gave his fortune to the first man he met in the morning, he would get well. The sneaky man planned to wait for the king outside the palace in the morning.

---

7.   American scientists and a champion Greek bicycle rider worked together to make an airplane powered by pedaling. The scientists designed the light plane with special pedals that would turn its propeller. The strongest bicycle rider was chosen. The bicyclist had to pedal constantly to keep the airplane in the air!

---

8.   A giant clothespin is in the center of Philadelphia and is higher than a four-story building. It is made of steel and weighs as much as five automobiles. Of course, the giant clothespin is not used to hang clothes. It is a monument. The artist Claes Oldenburg made the structure.

---

9.   According to records, Smith is the most common last name in the United States. Why is Smith more common than any other name? Long ago any craftsperson who used a hammer was named Smith. So many craftspeople used hammers to work with wood, metal, and stone that the name Smith became common.

---

10.   The 1889 World's Fair was held in Paris, France. The planners of the fair wanted to get everyone's attention. They requested the help of Alexander Eiffel, a bridge builder. He built a tower of iron bars 984 feet tall. It was called the Eiffel Tower. The visitors to the fair were thrilled.

6. You can tell that
  (A) the sneaky man wanted the fortune for himself.
  (B) the king would feel better after he gave his fortune to the sneaky man.
  (C) the sneaky man would take the fortune and give it to charity.

---

7. You can tell that
  (A) the special plane can stay in the air forever.
  (B) the plane would land when the bicycle rider got tired.
  (C) the special plane was very heavy.

---

8. You can tell that
  (A) everyone likes looking at the clothespin structure.
  (B) nobody can see the clothespin structure.
  (C) the clothespin structure can be seen from far away.

---

9. You can tell that
  (A) many people have changed their name to Smith.
  (B) not many Smiths are left in the world.
  (C) the name Smith no longer tells what someone's job is.

---

10. You can tell that
  (A) the Eiffel Tower was named after its builder.
  (B) the Eiffel Tower was torn down shortly after the 1889 World's Fair.
  (C) nobody liked the Eiffel Tower at first.

ADVANCED TEST • DRAWING CONCLUSIONS

1.   Richard Blechynden, a young Englishman, was displaying teas from Asia at the 1904 World's Fair. He had come all the way from Calcutta, India, to St. Louis, Missouri, to help serve tea to visitors in order to make tea more popular. The weather in St. Louis was sweltering. The crowds didn't show much interest in being served hot tea. People headed instead for cold drinks or ice cream. Richard Blechynden began to experiment. *If people wanted iced drinks,* he thought, *why not try iced tea?* He filled some tall glasses with ice cubes, poured in hot tea, and waited a few minutes. People tried it and liked it. Iced tea became a very popular summer drink.

2.   As an editor for *The Old Farmer's Almanac,* Martha White has a head full of odd bits of information related to the seasons, the weather, and many other things. She knows that the Native American name for the spring moon is the Full Worm Moon. This refers to the fact that in spring, worms' bodies grow fat and robins return to feast on them. She knows the language of flowers (white roses mean "silence"; carnations mean "love"), the size of a five-penny nail, and the fact that squirrels forget where they have hidden half their nuts. She loves hunting for these odd facts and sharing them with the almanac's readers.

3.   Roberta awoke to the feel of the train car gliding across the tracks. Yawning, she peered out the window at the Italian countryside. "Next stop, Padova," the train conductor announced. "Padova?" Roberta replied, a look of panic seizing her face. Opening her map, she searched for the unfamiliar town. Then she scanned for Verona, the home of her friend and her final destination. "Oh, no!" Roberta gasped. Her watch offered even more bad news. Grabbing her backpack and a colorfully wrapped gift, Roberta headed for the train door.

4.   For four hours two men molded the material into the shape of a Norse warrior pulled by four polar bears. After they finished, the watching crowd burst into loud applause. Gerry Kirk and Todd Vander Pluym were declared winners and awarded $5,000 in prize money. The building material they used was sand. The occasion was the Canadian Open Sand Castle Competition in White Rock, British Columbia. The winners are professional sand castlers, or people who build sand castles. Their work is in demand by movie studios, tourist bureaus, and other organizations eager for publicity. Kirk and Vander Pluym have been paid to build a host of magnificent sand castles all over the country.

5.   Catching the school bus to Madison High School seemed embarrassing to Joe. Now sixteen, Joe was determined to buy his own car. He landed an after-school job at a grocery store. Working fifteen hours a week for four months, Joe saved enough money to buy a car. He searched through the newspaper, scanning classified ads for used vehicles. Unfortunately, the best cars cost more than Joe could afford. Three months later Joe used his own money to buy a car with a good engine and a brand-new stereo.

ADVANCED TEST • DRAWING CONCLUSIONS

1. You can tell that
   (A) Richard Blechynden lived in England.
   (B) iced tea quickly became more popular than ice cream.
   (C) iced tea was popular at the 1904 World's Fair.
   (D) iced tea is the most popular drink sold in America.

2. You can tell that
   (A) *The Old Farmer's Almanac* contains facts about the seasons and the weather.
   (B) Martha White is sixty years old.
   (C) worms live only in the springtime.
   (D) a five-penny nail is very small.

3. You can tell that
   (A) Roberta bought the wrong train ticket.
   (B) Roberta fell asleep on the train.
   (C) Roberta could not speak Italian.
   (D) Roberta went shopping and missed her train.

4. You can tell that
   (A) sand castles can only be built in Canada.
   (B) no one is interested in sand castles.
   (C) anyone can build an elaborate sand castle.
   (D) sand castles can be elaborate and take hours to build.

5. You can tell that
   (A) Joe borrowed the money from his parents.
   (B) Joe sold his bicycle for extra money.
   (C) Joe received a discount on the car.
   (D) Joe worked and saved more money.

6.   Your ability to react quickly and to perform certain tasks can be impaired by various factors—illness or lack of sleep, for example. Studies of people suffering from colds and flu have been conducted at the Medical Research Council's Common Cold Unit in Salisbury, England. These studies showed that people with flu symptoms took 57 percent longer to react to targets on video games than people in good health did. People with cold symptoms were less able than healthy people to track the moving targets. Their hands did not respond accurately to the information their eyes gave them.

7.   In 1850 Elizabeth Smith Miller decided that she had had enough of the clothing that women of her day were expected to wear. She was gardening in the hot sun and wearing stays—stiff strips pulled tight to make her waist small. Over the stays she wore five long petticoats and a long dress. Not only was she unbearably hot, but she found it difficult to bend or move in her clothing. Miller made herself a pair of loose-fitting pants that tied at the ankle. Over these she wore a dress that hung four inches below the knee and did not pull in at the waist. Most people were shocked at Elizabeth Miller's outfit, but some women made similar outfits in order to be comfortable.

8.   Laws are sometimes passed to solve a particular problem or govern a particular situation. Long after the problem or situation has disappeared, the law may remain. For example, a law in Ziegler, Illinois, says that the first four firefighters to arrive at a fire will be paid. This law was probably passed at a time when the city could not afford full-time firefighters and depended on citizens to hurry to fight fires when they broke out. Some laws seem really strange, but if you think about them, you understand the reasons they were passed. For example, a law in Reed City, Michigan, prohibits owning both a bird and a cat.

9.   For many years scientists have wondered how much of a person's behavior and personality is inherited and how much is learned. Many identical twins who are raised apart act strikingly similar, even when they have never met. Jim Springer and Jim Lewis were separated as infants and did not meet until they were 39 years old. They discovered they drove blue cars of the same make and model and spent their vacations at the same beach. Each had a first wife named Linda and then a second wife named Betty. The men's first sons were named James Allen and James Alan. Both men named their dogs Toy.

10.   Mark Anderson's friend Kassie picks up after him, carries his book bag, and gets his mother if he is hurt. Nine-year-old Mark was born with a condition of the spine that keeps him in a wheelchair. Kassie is a dog—a Labrador retriever that was specially trained by a group that provides canine helpers for people with special needs. Mark and Kassie went to camp for two weeks to learn to work together. Kassie obeys eighty-nine different commands. Kassie is allowed to stay with Mark in class. Having Kassie has made a whole range of new activities possible for Mark.

6. You can tell that
   (A) many people are tired in Salisbury, England.
   (B) your body slows down when you are sick.
   (C) 57 percent of the people studied were tired.
   (D) video games are made in Salisbury, England.

7. You can tell that
   (A) Elizabeth Miller was thin.
   (B) only men were allowed to garden in 1850.
   (C) Elizabeth Miller wanted to wear cooler clothes.
   (D) her petticoats were decorated with ruffles and lace.

8. You can tell that
   (A) some laws that seem strange today were, at one time, passed for a reason.
   (B) people should always abide by laws.
   (C) Reed City, Michigan, has no cats.
   (D) many people want to be firefighters.

9. You can tell that
   (A) blue is the most popular color for a car.
   (B) Jim Springer and Jim Lewis are identical twins
   (C) Linda is a popular name.
   (D) James Allen and James Alan are identical twins.

10. You can tell that
   (A) Kassie has black hair.
   (B) Mark is very smart.
   (C) Kassie helps Mark in many ways.
   (D) Kassie barks a lot.

SEQUENCING

Special Instructions

1. Students should first read the passage carefully. Without looking at the passage, they should be able to recall the sequence in which the events occurred. If they cannot do this, they should reread the passage before attempting to answer the questions. In answering, students may look at the passage as often as necessary.

2. It should be emphasized to students that a question asking "Which happened first?" or "Which happened last?" means "Which happened first [last] among the given answer choices?" (not "Which happened first [last] in the entire passage?").

Answer Sheet Blackline Masters for tests in this skill strand:

    Primary Test: Use Answer Sheet 3.

    Intermediate Test: Use Answer Sheet 4.

    Advanced Test: Use Answer Sheet 4.

PLACEMENT TABLE

	Raw Score (Number Correct)	Book Placement
Primary Test	0–1	Picture
	2	Preparatory
	3–4	A
	5–6	B
	7–8	C
Intermediate Test	3–4	D
	5–7	E
	8–10	F
Advanced Test	5–7	G
	8–10	H

Tara and Oskar decided to have a funny race. First, they hopped three times on one foot and three times on the other foot. Next, they jumped four times. Then, they walked six steps facing backward. By the time they finished, they were laughing. In fact, they laughed so hard they did not even know who won. They were having fun.

1. What happened first?
  (A) Tess and Oskar hopped.
  (B) Tess and Oskar laughed.
  (C) Tess and Oskar jumped.

Chin ran to the beach with a loaf of stale bread. As soon as the gulls spotted her, they flew up close. Chin broke the bread into small bits and tossed them into the air. The gulls swooped in for their share. When all the bread was gone, Chin walked home. The next day she would be back, and so would the gulls.

2. What happened first?
  (A) Chin tossed bread to the gulls.
  (B) Chin walked home.
  (C) Chin ran to the beach.

Sharda and Devin went to the farm. They wanted to pick pumpkins. Sharda found a big pumpkin. Devin chose a small pumpkin. Their dad carved the pumpkins. They put them on the porch.

3. What did they do last?

    (A) They went to the pumpkin farm.

    (B) They put the pumpkins on the porch.

    (C) Dad carved the pumpkins.

Ben and Chad wanted to camp in their backyard. They set up a tent in a soft, flat place. Then they laid their sleeping bags on the tent floor. Soon it grew dark, but the boys could not sleep. The sounds of the night made them toss and turn. Cats howled, bugs buzzed, and twigs snapped. The boys picked up their gear and went into the house.

4. What happened last?

    (A) The boys set up their tent.

    (B) The boys picked up their gear and went into the house.

    (C) The night sounds made the boys toss and turn.

"The dog is muddy, Jason," Mom called. "He needs a bath before he comes into the house. It is a nice day. Please give Rags a bath outside."

Jason got a large tub and an old towel. He filled the tub and called Rags. "Here Rags. Let me take your collar off," said John.

Rags backed away. He knew what was next. Jason spoke softly to calm his dog. Jason put him into the water.

Then Jason put shampoo on Rags and rubbed it into the dog's hair. Then he rinsed off the shampoo. Jason lifted Rags out of the tub and reached for the towel. Jason wasn't quick enough.

Rags tried to shake the water off. Water sprayed everywhere. Jason asked, "Rags, who has more water on him, you or me?"

---

5. Which of these things happened first?
   (A) Jason calmed Rags.
   (B) Jason put Rags into the tub.
   (C) Jason got a towel.

6. What happened right after Rags's bath?
   (A) Jason put the tub away.
   (B) Jason used a towel to dry Rags.
   (C) Rags shook the water off.

Rose loved animals. She knew a lot about them. "I want to be an animal doctor when I grow up," she would say. Everyone knew they could ask Rose about wild animals. "I'll ask Rose," they would say.

One day Jill saw a rabbit that was hurt. Jill ran to Rose's house. She knocked on the door. "Come quickly, Rose," cried Jill. "You will know what to do."

Rose ran to the rabbit that was hurt. It was in the yard. "I need strong cardboard. Get something to keep it warm too," she said. Jill ran fast to get those things. Rose spoke softly to the hurt animal.

Before long, Rose held the rabbit. It was on the cardboard. Rose kept still. She whispered to Jill, "We need to be quiet. We should not scare the rabbit. Let's take it to an animal doctor."

---

7. What happened first?

    (A) Rose held the rabbit.

    (B) Jill told Rose about the rabbit.

    (C) The rabbit was hurt.

8. What did Rose do first?

    (A) She said she needed a blanket.

    (B) She said she needed some cardboard.

    (C) She looked at the rabbit.

Mae Jemison was born on October 17, 1956, in Decatur, Alabama. When she was just three years old, her family moved to Chicago. Even when Jemison was very young, she liked science. She was very interested in how things worked.

Jemison graduated from high school when she was sixteen years old. She decided to study chemical engineering at Stanford University. People who study engineering learn how things work. Because Jemison is African American, she also decided to study about Africa and African Americans. While she was at Stanford, she learned to speak Swahili, an African language. She also learned to speak Japanese and Russian.

Jemison decided to become a medical doctor. She studied medicine at Cornell University. She worked as a doctor in Los Angeles in 1982. Then in 1983 she went to Africa to work as a doctor. When she came back to the United States in 1985, she applied to be an astronaut. Soon after Jemison applied, a terrible accident occurred. A space shuttle exploded. For a while part of the space program was shut down. Meanwhile, Jemison continued to work as a doctor. Finally, in June 1987, she became one of fifteen astronauts accepted into the space program.

Jemison went to Houston, Texas, to train as an astronaut. For about a year, she and the other astronauts worked for many hours every day. They learned how the shuttle worked. They studied astronomy and other sciences. They practiced flying in a shuttle model.

In 1989, Jemison was chosen to fly a space mission on the space shuttle *Endeavour*. Jemison and the other *Endeavour* astronauts trained especially for that flight. Jemison's job was to do experiments while in space. On September 12, 1992, the *Endeavour* lifted off from Earth. Mae Jemison became the first African American woman to go into space.

INTERMEDIATE TEST • SEQUENCING

1. When did Jemison move to Chicago?
   (A) When she was born
   (B) Before she lived in Decatur
   (C) After she lived in Decatur

---

2. What happened before Jemison went to Stanford University?
   (A) She graduated from high school.
   (B) She learned to speak Swahili.
   (C) She studied chemical engineering.

---

3. Which of these events happened first?
   (A) Jemison went to medical school.
   (B) A space shuttle exploded.
   (C) Jemison went to Africa.

---

4. When did Jemison go to Houston, Texas?
   (A) After she practiced flying in a shuttle model
   (B) After she trained as an astronaut
   (C) After she was accepted into the space program

---

5. Which of these events happened last?
   (A) Jemison went to Texas.
   (B) Jemison went into space.
   (C) Jemison went to Africa.

Wilma was six months old when she came to the United States. A circus family bought the baby elephant. They owned several other elephants. These elephants became Wilma's family. Her owners took wonderful care of her. They fed her fresh hay and grass and made sure she had plenty of clean water for drinking and bathing.

The circus family performed for huge crowds. They taught Wilma to hold onto the tail of the elephant in front of her as they made circles around the tent. Wilma was a favorite with the adults and children who came to the circus.

Wilma performed with her circus family and the other elephants for many years. When she grew up, she was no longer the baby elephant at the end of the elephant parade. She learned to wear a fancy harness and blanket on her back. Her handlers taught her tricks. When they touched her right leg with a stick she sat down. When they touched her left leg she knelt down and let a girl climb onto her shoulders. Wilma's owners said she was the perfect elephant. She was kind and gentle. She was very careful not to hurt her handlers and did everything they asked of her.

At forty years old Wilma had seen many changes. Her handler's children had grown up and now took care of her. However, her new handlers became worried that she was too old for the circus. Her eyesight had dimmed, and the winters were very hard for her. Wilma deserved a wonderful place to retire. Her handlers looked and looked. At last they found a place in sunny California. It was a haven for retired circus animals. She would have acres of grassy hills and a pond with a waterfall. Wilma went there to live. Her handlers visit her. On nice days children visit the farm, and Wilma performs tricks just for them.

6. Which of these events happened first?
    (A) Wilma's eyesight dimmed, and the winters were hard on her.
    (B) Wilma came to the United States to be in the circus.
    (C) Wilma held onto the tail of the elephant in front of her.

7. Which of these events happened last?
    (A) Wilma performed tricks for children who visited her.
    (B) Wilma knelt down and let a girl climb on her back.
    (C) Wilma performed with the circus family for many years.

8. When did Wilma's handlers worry that she was too old for the circus?
    (A) When she joined the circus
    (B) When she was forty years old
    (C) When she came to the United States

9. When did the handlers' children take care of Wilma?
    (A) After Wilma retired
    (B) When Wilma first came to the United States
    (C) When they grew up

10. Where was the last place Wilma lived?
    (A) In a circus tent
    (B) With a circus family
    (C) At a farm for retired circus animals

Rachel Carson was born in 1907 in Pennsylvania. She always wanted to be a writer, even as a child. Her story "A Battle in the Clouds" was printed in *St. Nicholas* magazine in 1918. She was paid $10.00 for her story.

Rachel studied literature in college but also had to take some science courses in order to graduate. Her biology teacher, Mary Scott Skinker, taught her subject with so much passion that Rachel decided to change her major to biology. But she loved writing too. Would she have to choose between the two?

Carson earned a master's degree in marine biology from Johns Hopkins University in 1932, but there were few jobs for women scientists in those days. She began writing radio scripts for the Bureau of Fisheries. This work paid about $20.00 per week. Carson was thrilled to find a job in which she could combine science with writing. Later a full-time job paying $2,000 per year opened at the Bureau.

Soon Carson's writing was in great demand. *Under the Sea Wind,* a book about the creatures of the sea, was published in 1941. It combined fictional stories about sea animals and plants with factual science in an interesting way. Not many writers could do that. *The Sea around Us* followed ten years later.

Carson began to learn about the environmental threats to life both in the oceans and on land. She studied the effects of pesticides used to control mosquitoes and other insect pests. DDT had indeed reduced diseases carried by mosquitoes, but it was also killing bees, grasshoppers, birds, and other animals.

In 1962 Carson published *Silent Spring*. The title was inspired by the fact that pesticides were reducing bird and wildlife populations, making each spring more silent than the last. The book caused a tremendous controversy. Chemical manufacturers called Carson a hysterical woman and worse. Others were supportive. Scientists praised the accuracy of her research. The *New York Times* said she should win the Nobel Prize. President John F. Kennedy read the book and set up an advisory committee to investigate the dangers of pesticide misuse. Carson testified before a Senate committee in 1963.

The use of DDT was severely restricted in 1972 by the Environmental Protection Agency, which was formed in 1970. Many people feel that Carson's work led to the formation of the EPA. Unfortunately, Carson did not live to see the results of her efforts. She died of cancer in 1964.

1. What happened first?
- **(A)** *Under the Sea Wind* was published.
- **(B)** *Silent Spring* was published.
- **(C)** *The Sea around Us* was published.
- **(D)** "A Battle in the Clouds" was published.

2. When did Rachel Carson decide she wanted to be a writer?
- **(A)** After she graduated from Johns Hopkins University
- **(B)** After she decided to study biology
- **(C)** When she was a child
- **(D)** After the success of *The Sea around Us*

3. When did Rachel Carson fall in love with science?
- **(A)** When she had Mary Scott Skinker as a teacher
- **(B)** When she began to research DDT
- **(C)** When she decided to combine writing and science
- **(D)** When she was taking literature courses

4. What happened last?
- **(A)** DDT was restricted.
- **(B)** The EPA was formed.
- **(C)** Rachel Carson published *Silent Spring*.
- **(D)** Rachel Carson testified before Congress.

5. When did Rachel Carson make about $20.00 per week?
- **(A)** When she was writing for *St. Nicholas* magazine
- **(B)** When she published *Silent Spring*
- **(C)** When she worked full-time with the Bureau of Fisheries
- **(D)** When she wrote radio scripts for the Bureau of Fisheries

ADVANCED TEST • SEQUENCING

You might guess that chewing gum is an activity known only in the modern world. But chewing gum is not all that new.

The ancient Greeks, whose civilization flourished from 479 to 338 B.C., are known for their contributions to culture. Could chewing gum be counted among them? They chewed a substance called *mastiche,* which was derived from the resin of a mastic tree. Ancient Mayans were busy chewers as well. They chewed something called *chicle,* which is the sap from a sapodilla tree. The Mayan civilization peaked from A.D. 300 to 800. Native Americans farther north had long chewed the sap from spruce trees. When English settlers began arriving in the 1600s, native people passed the custom on to them.

Then, in 1848, chewing gum hit the stores. John Curtis made and sold a gum that he called "State of Maine Pure Spruce Gum." For most people, chewing gum still had a long way to go in terms of taste and texture. Two years later Curtis began marketing a flavored gum made with paraffin, which was more popular.

Meanwhile, Antonio Lopez de Santa Anna, the Mexican General who conquered the Alamo in 1836, enjoyed his favorite chew—the chicle favored by the Mayans and Aztecs. It didn't have much taste, but it did exercise the jaw muscles. Later, when Santa Anna moved to Staten Island in New York, he introduced chicle to Thomas Adams. In 1871 Adams patented a machine for manufacturing the gum. He sold small balls of flavorless gum for a penny each. Then a few years later, a Kentucky drugstore owner named John Colgan added long-lasting flavor to improve the gum he sold.

Not to be outdone, Adams added sassafras-licorice flavoring to gum he called "Black Jack." Then, in 1888, he added a fruit flavor to his gum that he called "Tutti Frutti," which he sold in vending machines in a New York City subway station.

Improvements continued, and in 1906 Frank Fleer invented the first bubble gum. He called it "Blibber-Blubber." It required a higher surface tension to produce the bubbles. His gum was never sold, but his brother Henry Fleer produced a gum consisting of small squares covered by a candy coating. His gum, first sold in 1910, became very popular.

Meanwhile, William Wrigley Jr., a former soap salesman, was busy at work developing his own brand of gum. In 1892 he introduced mint- and fruit-flavored varieties to the market. His technical advances changed the industry, and the gum remains popular worldwide.

6. Which of these happened first?

   (A) The civilization of the ancient Mayans peaked.

   (B) Ancient Greek civilization flourished.

   (C) English settlers arrived in North America.

   (D) Native Americans introduced chewing gum to settlers.

---

7. When did General Santa Anna introduce chicle to Thomas Adams?

   (A) Before conquering the Alamo

   (B) After Adams had patented a machine to make chewing gum

   (C) After he moved to Staten Island

   (D) Before John Curtis sold State of Maine Pure Spruce Gum

---

8. When did Thomas Adams add sassafras-licorice flavor to his gum?

   (A) After John Colgan added long-lasting flavor to his gum

   (B) After selling his gum in vending machines

   (C) Right around the time bubble gum was invented

   (D) Before he sold balls of gum for a penny each

---

9. Which happened last?

   (A) William Wrigley Jr. sold soap.

   (B) Frank Fleer invented bubble gum.

   (C) William Wrigley Jr. developed his own gum.

   (D) Henry Fleer sold candy coated gum squares.

---

10. Which best describes the general sequence of events that took place after people first chewed natural substances?

   (A) People added flavoring and artificial ingredients but eventually went back to chewing natural substances.

   (B) People began selling gum, adding flavors, and then making improvements to the taste and texture of gum.

   (C) Gum chewing in modern times became socially acceptable when people learned that the ancient Greeks chewed gum.

   (D) People first perfected the taste and texture of gum and then began to market it.

MAKING INFERENCES

Special Instructions

1. It must be emphasized to students that they are to arrive at probable conclusions from a limited amount of information, utilizing previously acquired knowledge and past experiences to fully comprehend the message of the text.

2. In Exercises 1–4 of the Primary test, students are to determine which one of the statements accompanying each passage is a valid inference. Thereafter, students are to determine whether each statement in the set accompanying a passage is a true statement, a false statement, or a valid inference. There may be any number of true statements, false statements, or inferences in a set.

Answer Sheet Blackline Masters for tests in this skill strand:

    Primary Test: Use Answer Sheet 3.

    Intermediate Test: Use Answer Sheet 6.

    Advanced Test: Use Answer Sheet 6.

PLACEMENT TABLE

	Raw Score (Number Correct)	Book Placement
Primary Test	0–1	Picture
	2	Preparatory
	3–4	A
	5–6	B
	7–8	C
Intermediate Test	3–4	D
	5–7	E
	8–10	F
Advanced Test	5–7	G
	8–10	H

"Mom! I hurt my hand," called Horatio. His mom looked at Horatio's hand. It had a large bruise. Behind Horatio was his bicycle. It was lying on the sidewalk.

1. Which of the following is probably true?

(A) Horatio fell off his bicycle.

(B) Horatio does not like to ride his bicycle.

(C) Horatio has a nice bicycle.

Manuel went to the petting zoo with his sister. At the zoo they saw some horses and goats. Manuel fed some grass to the goats. The goats ate the grass out of his hand. Manuel smiled.

2. Which of the following is probably true?

(A) Manuel wanted to ride a horse.

(B) Goats make good pets.

(C) Manuel liked feeding the goats.

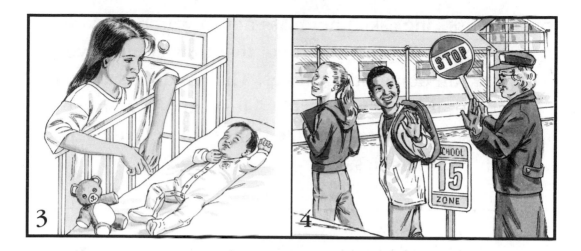

Elena's baby was crying. Elena thought he was hungry. She gave him some food. He did not eat. She gave him something to drink. He would not drink. She took him for a walk. Still he cried and cried. Finally, Elena started to sing. The baby stopped crying.

3. Which of the following is probably true?
   (A) The baby does not like to go for walks.
   (B) The baby does not like to drink.
   (C) The baby likes the sound of Elena's voice.

Many cars go by Jane's school. For 20 years, Mrs. Singer had helped the children go across the street. Now Mrs. Singer was going to stop working. Jane said, "Mrs. Singer has helped children for many years. We should do something for her."

4. Which of the following is probably true?
   (A) The children like Mrs. Singer.
   (B) Mrs. Singer does not like her job.
   (C) Jane has many friends.

5.   Miss Ling asked her class not to watch television for one week. She told them that they could have more fun doing other things. The children said, "Let's find out if Miss Ling is right." Instead of watching television, they read, made things, and played games with their families.

---

6.   Mr. Garcia loves to fish. One day when he was fishing, a neighbor came to watch him. Mr. Garcia asked, "Don't you like to fish?" His neighbor, Lucy, said that she liked to fish but she didn't have a fishing pole. Mr. Garcia bought her a fishing pole.

---

7.   Justin got into the car. He carried a brightly colored box. "I hope his dad made a big cake," he said. When they got to Adam's house, they saw many boys running up to the door with bags and boxes.

---

8.   The boys and girls were talking and laughing. They were in line to get on the bus. They would be at the park soon. A park worker would lead them to the creek. The boys and girls would look for things in the creek.

5. Which of the following is probably true?

    (A) Miss Ling wants to watch television now.

    (B) Miss Ling is a teacher.

    (C) Miss Ling was wrong.

---

6. Which of the following is probably true?

    (A) Lucy will go fishing with Mr. Garcia.

    (B) Mr. Garcia does not want Lucy to watch him.

    (C) Lucy never went fishing before.

---

7. Which of the following is probably true?

    (A) Justin is late.

    (B) Justin is going to a birthday party.

    (C) Justin's mother made a cake.

---

8. Which of the following is probably true?

    (A) The park worker does not like the bus.

    (B) Nothing lives in the creek.

    (C) The children were on a field trip.

1.   In 1947 a sailor named Thor Heyerdahl sailed a wooden raft across the Pacific Ocean. Heyerdahl believed that people from South America sailed to Polynesia thousands of years earlier. He made his journey to prove that those early people could have made the trip. On another trip Heyerdahl tried to establish that Egyptians could have sailed to America more than two thousand years ago.

2.   The rocks in the petrified forest are actually trees that died a very long time ago. When they died, they sank into watery soil and absorbed minerals from the soil. Over time, the water disappeared. The minerals had become part of the trees, so the trees turned into stone.

3.   In the early 1800s only a few people, called mountain men, had settled in the Rocky Mountains. As they moved around, these people found many passes through the mountains. They also learned the paths of the rivers. Because of their special knowledge, many mountain men became guides for settlers who traveled over the Rocky Mountains.

4.   Weather vanes show the direction of the wind. The first weather vanes were used by the Greeks almost two thousand years ago. You can see weather vanes shaped like lions, tigers, pigs, and even automobiles. They are used on farms, boats, and at weather stations. Some people collect weather vanes and keep them indoors.

5.   Not all birds migrate south in winter to warmer places. Birds such as the northern cardinal stay north because they find enough food to eat all winter long. Other birds stick around but leave when it gets cold. Hardy snowy owls may stay or leave, depending on how much food they can find.

INTERMEDIATE TEST • MAKING INFERENCES

	T	F	I
1. (A) Thor Heyerdahl was a good sailor and historian.	☐	☐	☐
(B) Thor Heyerdahl believed that people from South America sailed to Polynesia.	☐	☐	☐
(C) Thor Heyerdahl was a brave adventurer.	☐	☐	☐
(D) Thor Heyerdahl sailed across the Bering Strait.	☐	☐	☐

	T	F	I
2. (A) The rocks in the petrified forest are actually old bones.	☐	☐	☐
(B) The trees in the forest sank into the watery soil and absorbed minerals.	☐	☐	☐
(C) It took millions of years for trees to turn into stone.	☐	☐	☐
(D) The rocks in a petrified forest are half stone and half water.	☐	☐	☐

	T	F	I
3. (A) Mountain men became guides for other settlers traveling in the Rocky Mountains.	☐	☐	☐
(B) Mountain men were familiar with mountain passes and rivers.	☐	☐	☐
(C) In the early 1500s, early mountain men settled in the Rocky Mountains.	☐	☐	☐
(D) The mountain men were experts on the terrain of the Rocky Mountains.	☐	☐	☐

	T	F	I
4. (A) People collect weather vanes because they are interesting and creative.	☐	☐	☐
(B) Weather vanes show the direction of the wind.	☐	☐	☐
(C) The first weather vanes were used by the English in 1745.	☐	☐	☐
(D) Some people collect weather vanes.	☐	☐	☐

	T	F	I
5. (A) The northern cardinal is a bird that does not migrate south.	☐	☐	☐
(B) One reason birds migrate is to find food.	☐	☐	☐
(C) Snowy owls cannot survive in cold weather.	☐	☐	☐
(D) Some birds stay north as long as they find food to eat.	☐	☐	☐

6.   A family in Massachusetts found a duck nesting near their pool. It was raising a duckling and teaching it to swim in the pool! The family wanted to return the ducks to the wild. Because some kinds of ducks are protected by state law, a state officer wouldn't let the ducks be moved.

---

7.   Every morning Mrs. Brock gets up in Ohio and goes to Indiana to cook breakfast. Then she goes back to Ohio, wakes up her family, and all of them go to Indiana to eat. The Brocks don't do a lot of traveling every morning, though. They don't even leave their house!

---

8.   In a town in Indiana, a six-foot aspen tree is growing out of the clock tower on the courthouse roof. A bird or the wind probably carried the seed to the roof. It grew because the slate roof holds moisture. The slate also contains a mineral that helps feed the tree.

---

9.   Waxed cardboard milk containers are used to build boats for the Milk Carton Derby in Seattle, Washington. Each entry is made from empty milk cartons that are sealed tight with tape or glue. Then each sealed carton is tested for leaks. The winning boat must float the longest and go the farthest.

---

10.   Mrs. Fordyce was preparing dinner when she heard a knock at her door. She went to answer it and saw the neighbor's sheep butting its head against the door. Mrs. Fordyce called the police. The sheep broke through the door and began chasing her. Soon the police came and captured the sheep.

INTERMEDIATE TEST • MAKING INFERENCES

			T	**F**	**I**

6. **(A)** A family in Massachusetts found a duck nesting near their pool. ☐ ☐ ☐

(B) The family did not want the duck living in their pool. ☐ ☐ ☐

(C) The duck was teaching the duckling how to swim in the lake behind the house. ☐ ☐ ☐

(D) Some ducks are protected by state law. ☐ ☐ ☐

                                                                    T F I

7. **(A)** Every morning Mrs. Brock wakes up in Indiana. ☐ ☐ ☐

(B) The Brock family's house sits on the Ohio/Indiana state line. ☐ ☐ ☐

(C) Every morning Mrs. Brock cooks breakfast in Ohio. ☐ ☐ ☐

(D) The Brock family wakes up in Ohio. ☐ ☐ ☐

                                                                    T F I

8. **(A)** An aspen tree is growing out of a clock tower in an Indiana town. ☐ ☐ ☐

(B) The tree grew on the roof because the slate roof does not hold moisture. ☐ ☐ ☐

(C) A bird or the wind probably carried the seed to the roof. ☐ ☐ ☐

(D) If the roof were not made of slate, the tree probably could not grow there. ☐ ☐ ☐

                                                                    T F I

9. **(A)** The winning boat must float the longest and go the farthest. ☐ ☐ ☐

(B) The Milk Carton Derby takes place in Portland, Oregon. ☐ ☐ ☐

(C) Each empty milk carton is sealed tight with tape or glue. ☐ ☐ ☐

(D) Waxed cardboard milk cartons make good boats. ☐ ☐ ☐

                                                                    T F I

10. **(A)** The neighbor's sheep butted its head against Mrs. Fordyce's door. ☐ ☐ ☐

(B) Mrs. Fordyce chased the sheep out with a broom. ☐ ☐ ☐

(C) The neighbor's sheep was not friendly. ☐ ☐ ☐

(D) Mrs. Fordyce yelled at the sheep, and it went away. ☐ ☐ ☐

ADVANCED TEST • MAKING INFERENCES

1.   Sometimes old toys gather dust in attics for so many years that they become rare antiques. Emma and Archie Stiles of New Jersey collected rare and unusual toys for more than twenty-five years. Among their toys was a life-size horse from a merry-go-round, an eight-foot giraffe, two teddy bears from the days of President Teddy Roosevelt (after whom teddy bears were named), airplanes from the 1920s, trolley cars, sleds, and wooden bicycles. They bought the toys from antique dealers, private homes, flea markets, and garage sales.

2.   Doug and Dixie Sheldon of Los Angeles, California, travel by elevator from their home to their office. Both their condominium and their real estate office are in a city skyscraper. The Sheldons can go to a dry cleaner, a beauty salon, a pharmacy, a small grocery store, or a dentist without leaving the building. To reduce traffic and smog, the Community Redevelopment Agency (CRA) of Los Angeles has tried to encourage downtown workers to live near their jobs. The city had built low-cost housing where many downtown workers lived. To attract highly paid workers, the CRA helped build expensive condominium homes and apartments downtown. Now workers of all income levels are choosing to live downtown.

3.   Many people think that dogs and mail carriers don't get along very well. However, that isn't always the situation. One New York mail carrier said that he liked the three dogs that always followed him when he delivered mail around the neighborhood. They didn't bark or bite; they just ambled behind him. When he went into an apartment building, the dogs stayed outside and waited for him. At the end of the day, when all the mail was delivered, the carrier patted the dogs and went home. The next morning, all three dogs were waiting for him, eager to accompany him on his route once more.

4.   Two members of a California family opened a "bite-size" restaurant in Los Angeles. At this restaurant, thirty-two miniature items appear on the menu. They are common, popular foods, but each portion is tiny. Customers can order small salads, pizzas, hamburgers, tacos, and pitas. No bite-size item costs more than three dollars, and some cost less than a dollar. This "bite-size" restaurant became popular in its first year. People like the restaurant because it is friendly and because they do not need to choose between one favorite food and another.

5.   In 1847 engineers wanted to build a bridge across the Niagara Gorge, but they had a problem. No one could think of how to get the first cable across the river. Then someone had an idea—maybe a kite could be flown over the river. The kite string could be used to pull a rope across, and then the rope could be used to pull the first steel cable. The engineers offered five dollars to anyone who could fly a kite across the river. Many people tried and failed. Everyone went home except a young child who kept trying and finally succeeded. The youngster received the five dollars—and a place in history.

ADVANCED TEST • MAKING INFERENCES

	T	F	I
1. (A) The Stiles collected rare and unusual toys because they were valuable.	☐	☐	☐
(B) Emma and Archie Stiles lived in Tampa, Florida.	☐	☐	☐
(C) Teddy bears were named after President Teddy Roosevelt.	☐	☐	☐
(D) The Stiles owned a life-size horse from a merry-go-round.	☐	☐	☐

	T	F	I
2. (A) Only highly paid workers can afford to live in downtown Los Angeles.	☐	☐	☐
(B) Doug and Dixie Sheldon can go to a movie theater in their building.	☐	☐	☐
(C) The Sheldons enjoy living in the condominium because they can do many things in one building.	☐	☐	☐
(D) The CRA wanted to build condominiums downtown to help reduce traffic and smog.	☐	☐	☐

	T	F	I
3. (A) The mail carrier liked it when the dogs followed him.	☐	☐	☐
(B) The three dogs used to wait outside of apartment buildings for the mail carrier.	☐	☐	☐
(C) The mail carrier never touched the dogs.	☐	☐	☐
(D) The dogs used to bark loudly at the mail carrier.	☐	☐	☐

	T	F	I
4. (A) The "bite-size" restaurant is located in Montana.	☐	☐	☐
(B) The restaurant has never been very popular.	☐	☐	☐
(C) The restaurant's customers prefer eating many different foods during one meal.	☐	☐	☐
(D) No bite-size item at the restaurant costs more than three dollars.	☐	☐	☐

	T	F	I
5. (A) A prize of five dollars was offered to the winner of the kite-flying contest.	☐	☐	☐
(B) The child who won the kite-flying contest was excited.	☐	☐	☐
(C) The kite string was used to pull a rope across the gorge.	☐	☐	☐
(D) No one tried to fly a kite over the gorge because it would be too difficult.	☐	☐	☐

6.   Janet Sprik was feeling sad. While her husband was making deliveries, her dog, Sugar, jumped out of the truck and ran away. Mr. Sprik knew how much Janet loved the dog, so he spent two months checking every dog pound and animal shelter in the area. Sugar, however, was not to be found in a dog pound. She had run a few blocks from the truck to a house with some horses in the backyard. Sugar went to play with the horses, and the owners adopted her. Sugar lived there for eight months. Then one day a delivery truck drove into the driveway. Sugar began barking because the driver of the truck was Mr. Sprik.

7.   Clams are well protected from danger, but geoducks are even more cleverly adapted. As with other clams, the geoduck is a bivalve, meaning it has a soft, flat body that is protected by two hinged shells that open and close. Like other clams, geoducks bury themselves using their large foot to burrow into sand or mud. Their connection to the outside world is their neck, or siphon, that they use for sucking in food and water. Geoducks have an advantage because their siphons are longer than those of other clams. This allows them to bury themselves even deeper at the water's edge.

8.   When you think of a seed, do you think of something tiny? Many seeds are, especially those of strawberries and kiwi fruit. An avocado has one very large seed, or pit, the size of a golf ball. A new plant can be started from this pit. Suspend the avocado pit with toothpicks perched on a glass so the bottom two-thirds of the pit is always submerged in water. After a few weeks the pit develops a large crack. In a few more weeks, a root appears from the submerged end, followed in another week or so by a stem from the top. Finally the emerging plant can be planted in soil.

9.   Lacrosse is a game that was invented by Native Americans. Lacrosse has been popular in the United States and Canada since the 1800s. It is played on a field with opposing goals, similar to a soccer field. Players carry sticks with meshwork heads that act as scoops for the ball that may be carried, passed, or hit with the stick. Native Americans played the game for recreation and to settle disputes. Their games had anywhere from 100 to 1,000 players and might last up to three days!

10.   Bamboo is among the fastest-growing plants in existence. Some of its more than 1,000 species can grow more than 1½ feet in one day. Although bamboo looks like a slender tree, it is actually considered a grass. People use it to build furniture, houses, and even bridges. Bamboo is hollow, but it is incredibly strong. One suspension bridge over a river in China is 250 yards long. Built entirely without metal, it depends on bamboo cables for support. Bamboo spreads quickly, but if it is used carefully, it can prevent soil erosion, act as a windbreak, and help treat urban wastewater.

ADVANCED TEST • MAKING INFERENCES

		T	F	I
6.	(A) The Spriks gave Sugar to another family.	☐	☐	☐
	(B) Sugar jumped out of Mr. Sprik's truck.	☐	☐	☐
	(C) Sugar will not go on any more deliveries with Mr. Sprik.	☐	☐	☐
	(D) Sugar lived at the other house for ten months.	☐	☐	☐

		T	F	I
7.	(A) Geoducks and other clams are bivalves.	☐	☐	☐
	(B) Only geoducks have siphons.	☐	☐	☐
	(C) Staying buried keeps clams safe from predators.	☐	☐	☐
	(D) Clams need both food and water to survive.	☐	☐	☐

		T	F	I
8.	(A) A pit is a large seed.	☐	☐	☐
	(B) Kiwis have large seeds like those of avocados.	☐	☐	☐
	(C) An avocado pit is the size of a golf ball.	☐	☐	☐
	(D) To keep the pit wet, water should be added to the glass as needed.	☐	☐	☐

		T	F	I
9.	(A) In lacrosse, players may not pass the ball with the stick.	☐	☐	☐
	(B) Native American lacrosse games lasted longer than those of today.	☐	☐	☐
	(C) Native Americans taught lacrosse to European Americans.	☐	☐	☐
	(D) Lacrosse is played with a ball.	☐	☐	☐

		T	F	I
10.	(A) Bamboo is a type of grass.	☐	☐	☐
	(B) There are more than 2,000 species of bamboo.	☐	☐	☐
	(C) Bamboo can be used instead of metal in some instances.	☐	☐	☐
	(D) Some bamboo species grow 1½ feet in an hour.	☐	☐	☐

Answer Keys

USING PHONICS/USING WORD STUDY
Primary Test—Using Phonics

1.	5	13.	A
2.	2	14.	B
3.	9	15.	B
4.	4	16.	A
5.	3	17.	A
6.	1	18.	B
7.	10	19.	B
8.	11	20.	A
9.	14	21.	B
10.	17	22.	A
11.	13	23.	B
12.	15	24.	A

USING PHONICS/USING WORD STUDY
Intermediate Test—Using Word Study

1.	B	21.	B
2.	E	22.	E
3.	C	23.	C
4.	B	24.	E
5.	E	25.	C
6.	B	26.	E
7.	D	27.	E
8.	C	28.	B
9.	F	29.	A
10.	E	30.	D
11.	D	31.	A
12.	C	32.	E
13.	E	33.	A
14.	B	34.	C
15.	D	35.	D
16.	C	36.	B
17.	A	37.	D
18.	B	38.	E
19.	A	39.	D
20.	C	40.	B

USING PHONICS/USING WORD STUDY
Advanced Test—Using Word Study

1. A	21. B
2. C	22. A
3. A	23. C
4. C	24. B
5. B	25. A
6. C	26. C
7. B	27. B
8. A	28. A
9. A	29. C
10. C	30. A
11. C	31. B
12. A	32. C
13. B	33. A
14. C	34. B
15. B	35. C
16. A	36. B
17. B	37. A
18. A	38. A
19. C	39. C
20. B	40. B

GETTING THE MAIN IDEA
Primary Test

1. A	5. C
2. B	6. A
3. B	7. B
4. A	8. A

GETTING THE MAIN IDEA
Intermediate Test

1. C	6. C
2. B	7. C
3. B	8. A
4. C	9. B
5. C	10. B

GETTING THE MAIN IDEA
Advanced Test

1. D	6. C
2. D	7. D
3. C	8. D
4. B	9. C
5. A	10. B

FINDING DETAILS
Primary Test

1. C	6. C
2. B	7. B
3. A	8. A
4. A	9. B
5. C	10. B

FINDING DETAILS
Intermediate Test

1. B		11. B
2. A		12. A
3. B		13. C
4. C		14. A
5. A		15. B
6. C		16. C
7. B		17. C
8. A		18. A
9. B		19. B
10. A		20. A

FINDING DETAILS
Advanced Test

1. C		11. A
2. D		12. D
3. B		13. C
4. B		14. B
5. A		15. D
6. A		16. C
7. D		17. D
8. C		18. B
9. D		19. C
10. D		20. C

COMPARING & CONTRASTING
Primary Test

1. B	**5.** A
2. B	**6.** B
3. C	**7.** B
4. A	**8.** C

COMPARING & CONTRASTING
Intermediate Test

1. C	**6.** B
2. C	**7.** A
3. A	**8.** A
4. B	**9.** C
5. A	**10.** B

COMPARING & CONTRASTING
Advanced Test

1. B	**6.** D
2. C	**7.** C
3. D	**8.** A
4. A	**9.** D
5. D	**10.** B

IDENTIFYING CAUSE & EFFECT
Primary Test

1.	C	**5.**	B
2.	B	**6.**	A
3.	C	**7.**	C
4.	B	**8.**	B

IDENTIFYING CAUSE & EFFECT
Intermediate Test

1.	B	**6.**	A
2.	C	**7.**	B
3.	B	**8.**	B
4.	C	**9.**	C
5.	A	**10.**	C

IDENTIFYING CAUSE & EFFECT
Advanced Test

1.	C	**6.**	C
2.	A	**7.**	B
3.	C	**8.**	D
4.	A	**9.**	C
5.	C	**10.**	D

IDENTIFYING FACT & OPINION
Primary Test

1.	C	5.	C
2.	A	6.	C
3.	B	7.	A
4.	C	8.	C

IDENTIFYING FACT & OPINION
Intermediate Test

1.	A	6.	B
2.	B	7.	C
3.	C	8.	C
4.	C	9.	A
5.	B	10.	A

IDENTIFYING FACT & OPINION
Advanced Test

1.	C	6.	C
2.	A	7.	A
3.	C	8.	D
4.	C	9.	B
5.	D	10.	B

DRAWING CONCLUSIONS
Primary Test

1.	A	5.	B
2.	C	6.	C
3.	B	7.	B
4.	A	8.	A

DRAWING CONCLUSIONS
Intermediate Test

1.	C	6.	A
2.	B	7.	B
3.	A	8.	C
4.	B	9.	C
5.	A	10.	A

DRAWING CONCLUSIONS
Advanced Test

1.	C	6.	B
2.	A	7.	C
3.	B	8.	A
4.	D	9.	B
5.	D	10.	C

SEQUENCING
Primary Test

1.	A	5.	C
2.	C	6.	C
3.	B	7.	C
4.	B	8.	C

SEQUENCING
Intermediate Test

1.	C	6.	B
2.	A	7.	A
3.	A	8.	B
4.	C	9.	C
5.	B	10.	C

SEQUENCING
Advanced Test

1.	D	6.	B
2.	C	7.	C
3.	A	8.	A
4.	A	9.	C
5.	D	10.	B

MAKING INFERENCES
Primary Test

1.	A	5.	B
2.	C	6.	A
3.	C	7.	B
4.	A	8.	C

MAKING INFERENCES
Intermediate Test

1.	A.	I		6.	A.	T	
	B.	T			B.	I	
	C.	I			C.	F	
	D.	F			D.	T	
2.	A.	F		7.	A.	F	
	B.	T			B.	I	
	C.	I			C.	F	
	D.	F			D.	T	
3.	A.	T		8.	A.	T	
	B.	I			B.	F	
	C.	F			C.	T	
	D.	I			D.	I	
4.	A.	I		9.	A.	T	
	B.	T			B.	F	
	C.	F			C.	T	
	D.	T			D.	I	
5.	A.	T		10.	A.	T	
	B.	I			B.	F	
	C.	F			C.	I	
	D.	T			D.	F	

MAKING INFERENCES
Advanced Test

1. A. I
   B. F
   C. T
   D. T

2. A. F
   B. F
   C. I
   D. T

3. A. I
   B. T
   C. F
   D. F

4. A. F
   B. F
   C. I
   D. T

5. A. T
   B. I
   C. T
   D. F

6. A. F
   B. T
   C. I
   D. F

7. A. T
   B. F
   C. I
   D. I

8. A. T
   B. F
   C. T
   D. I

9. A. F
   B. T
   C. I
   D. T

10. A. T
    B. F
    C. I
    D. F

SPECIFIC SKILL SERIES
Assessment Answer Sheet 1

Student _____

Teacher _____

Date _____

Skill _____

Level ☐ **Primary**   ☐ **Intermediate**   ☐ **Advanced**

1		7		13		19	
2		8		14		20	
3		9		15		21	
4		10		16		22	
5		11		17		23	
6		12		18		24	

Raw Score _____   **Book Level** _____

SPECIFIC SKILL SERIES
Assessment Answer Sheet 2

Student _____

Teacher _____

Date _____

Skill _____

Level ☐ Primary   ☐ Intermediate   ☐ Advanced

1		11		21		31	
2		12		22		32	
3		13		23		33	
4		14		24		34	
5		15		25		35	
6		16		26		36	
7		17		27		37	
8		18		28		38	
9		19		29		39	
10		20		30		40	

Raw Score _____   Book Level _____

SPECIFIC SKILL SERIES
Assessment Answer Sheet 3

Student _____

Teacher _____

Date _____

Skill _____

Level ❑ Primary   ❑ Intermediate   ❑ Advanced

1		**5**	
2		**6**	
3		**7**	
4		**8**	

Raw Score _____   Book Level _____

SPECIFIC SKILL SERIES
Assessment Answer Sheet 4

Student _____

Teacher _____

Date _____

Skill _____

Level   ❏ **Primary**   ❏ **Intermediate**   ❏ **Advanced**

1		**6**	
2		**7**	
3		**8**	
4		**9**	
5		**10**	

Raw Score _____   **Book Level** _____

SPECIFIC SKILL SERIES
Assessment Answer Sheet 5

Student

Teacher

Date

Skill

Level ❑ Primary ❑ Intermediate ❑ Advanced

1		6		11		16	
2		7		12		17	
3		8		13		18	
4		9		14		19	
5		10		15		20	

Raw Score _____   Book Level _____

SPECIFIC SKILL SERIES
Assessment Answer Sheet 6

Student _____

Teacher _____

Date _____

Skill _____

Level ❏ **Primary**   ❏ **Intermediate**   ❏ **Advanced**

1			6		
	A			A	
	B			B	
	C			C	
	D			D	
2	A		7	A	
	B			B	
	C			C	
	D			D	
3	A		8	A	
	B			B	
	C			C	
	D			D	
4	A		9	A	
	B			B	
	C			C	
	D			D	
5	A		10	A	
	B			B	
	C			C	
	D			D	

Raw Score _____   **Book Level** _____

SPECIFIC SKILL SERIES · STUDENT PERFORMANCE PROFILE

Name _____ Class _____

School _____ City _____ State _____

Placement Tests: Primary _____ Intermediate _____ Advanced _____

Testing Dates _____

BOOKS

	Pict.	Prep.	A	B	C	D	E	F	G	H
Using Phonics/Using Word Study										
Getting the Main Idea										
Finding Details										
Comparing and Contrasting										
Identifying Cause and Effect										
Identifying Fact and Opinion										
Drawing Conclusions										
Sequencing										
Making Inferences										

Upon completion of each book, record the student's average score in the accompanying space.